The Cousin
is Sleeping
in PRAGUE

Contents

© Dagmar Štětinová, Prague 2000
Translation © David R. Beveridge, Prague 2000
Photographs © Miloslav Hušek, Prague 2005
Drawings © Jindra Kejř, Prague 2000
© Jitka Kejřová, V Ráji publishers, Prague 2000, 2005

ISBN 80-85894-76-9

The Golem
is Sleeping
in PRAGUE

The Golem
is Sleeping
in PRAGUE
Dagmar Štětinová

From the Talmud:

Heaven is against us for our sins,
but the world for our virtue.

From my wartime childhood, fleeing to the cellars upon the wailing of the sirens announcing the beginning and end of bombing raids on Prague, from the horrifying posters screaming as warning lists of those disobedient family members or even whole families who had violated the ban on listening to "London Calling" or "Moscow Speaks" on the radio, or who had expressed themselves incorrectly regarding "der Führer" and did not wish him victory, from that blue darkening of windows and souls, emerges a sweet memory of the face of the girl who lived in the building across our street. She appeared in that window regularly, a little girl with dark, curly hair with a big ribbon in the back. She showed me from afar her stuffed teddy bear, and blew soap bubbles out the window, and I showed her the tame crow that sat on my shoulder. We waved at each other and blew each other kisses.

One day I waited in vain. The girl, the Roubíček family's little doll, did not appear in the window. The window was closed all day, and the next day too. Why? It was summer, after all! Where had she gone? Where was she? I felt betrayed. What had I done to her? Why didn't she open the window? That day I had no breakfast. On the next few days, too, I waited in vain. The woman who took us on walks whispered to me: "She won't ever come again! Don't wait."

"Why?" I cried out, horrified.

"You wouldn't understand. It's better if you don't know," said the young woman. Then she added in a whisper: "They're Jews."

Soňa Roubíčková never returned again, nor did her older sister Katka. They had been transported somewhere else than their parents, but the whole family ended up the same way as millions of other victims of the holocaust and of that horrible and senseless war.

That window remained closed to me forever from the day when I found that out. But the heart never did. I don't separate people based on color of skin, but on the color of the heart. I don't argue with friends when they try to assert their beliefs, whether religious or intellectual. Let them be fans of this or that soccer team, let them believe in Buddha or Mohammed. I remain in the middle as the one who extends one hand to the east and the other to the west, and I would so much like to combine them in one single great, eternal handshake. I turn away only from people who honor neither God's nor man's morality, because that's a system that should be a signpost on the good path. I abandon those who pray and attend churches and temples of various faiths and claim that only they are right, whereas the others will be damned. In the name of their almighty they are capable even of murdering and hating. I resist hatred. It would suffocate my heart before it could finish serving my life.

"Who are the Jews?" asked many children when I was young, because it was not clear to them why they were so persecuted. How many parents could not manage to answer that question!

Only much later did I encounter people who were capable and for the most part intelligent who declared themselves to be Jews. I found out about the history of their nation and their customs, and they also told me the legends about their golem. The golem! He was a character in my children's fairy tales, which viewed him as they did dragons and other mythical beings.

Who actually was that golem and why did he come into existence? Was he a mythical being like a giant or a dragon, something between a headless knight, Hejkal, and Krakonoš? How did the golem serve people? Is he really sleeping, and can't he rise from the dead and be brought to life? What might happen then? As far as I know from the old Hebrew legend, the golem was rendered harmless and is sleeping eternally in the attic of the Old-New Synagogue. He did not ascend to heaven like Christ, and did not promise to return again on the Judgment Day. How long ago this all was! But for me to be able to engage in an exchange with the little curious one I have to remind myself of the whole story.

Princess Libuše's Prophecy

So what can we say about the golem and his creators? When did they give him life and transform that lifeless clay colossus into a helper and destroyer without a soul, using only fire and water? Why did he come into the world at the wish of the famous rabbi who wanted to help his people?

What we know from a true chronicler of the time tells us the amazing fact that Czech history was affected already in the early Middle Ages by the fate of the Jews, who came to our country in those long-ago times. It is said that Princess Libuše, as soon as she felt the time was coming for her to leave the earth and find her place among the stars, went out on the ramparts of Vyšehrad, accompanied at her right side by her son Nezamysl and on the left by Přemysl the Plower. For the last time the aging princess looked toward the horizon. She embraced her son and said to him:

"My most beloved! A strange image is appearing before my eyes in the mists of the future, where I am no longer among you, and your father too has left only his name here. But I see your face, Nezamysl, a manly face to which your son looks up. Beside you, your spouse is fondling the boy, whose name the gods have not revealed to me. But now the image is being covered over by another scene. Now your son is a man and is sitting on the princely throne and looking at his offspring to whom he will pass on his reign.

"And then," cried the agitated princess, "gods, what does this mean? Not fighting, not wars? No, this is not an armed people approaching the banks of the Vltava, but a great crowd of foreigners with families. They are coming to our country to find a refuge after the loss of their own country. They are not enemies. They want only work and a roof over their heads. They want to labor and to help our country and its people. But will your grandson on the princely throne give them what they need until better times come for them?"

Soon after this prophecy, Princess Libuše died, and among her last wishes was that he to whom a people without a country would turn for help would care for them just as she would.

When the time came, Nezamysl passed the reign on to his son, and the son to his own son, and at that time the prophecy became reality. Before the fateful day Libuše appeared to Hostivít in a princess's robe, beautiful and noble, and said to him:

"Welcome, new prince. I am your great grandmother. I ask that you, too, be good and just to the people, because tomorrow my prophecy of long ago is to be fulfilled."

"Yes," said Hostivít, "my father and grandfather told me about it. Rest assured, and return to your fathers and mine above the stars."

Early the next morning Hostivít heard voices in the courtyard. A crowd of people speaking a strange language were asking for an audience with the ruler of the land. Hostivít ordered that the crowd be quieted, that they be given bread with honey, and communicated that he would announce to them the decision of the whole council regarding the wish they had conveyed via a servant. In the manner of his ancestors, Hostivít made no decisions without his aldermen.

"What?" some exclaimed in horror. "Are we to allow such a large number of foreigners into our small country? Wouldn't it be better if they went where there are larger tracts of land?"

The prince lifted his hand to calm their agitation, and proclaimed:

"Long ago Princess Libuše, my great grandmother, foresaw this day, and with her last powers as a ruler she expressed the wish that we not refuse help to this crowd that would ask for a home. It is true that there are countries much broader and larger as far as space is concerned and the power of the people and riches of the treasuries. Our nation, however, has a great heart and, because of its Slavic nature, much compassion for those who suffer. Just look out the window! Mothers are holding their children to their breasts. Am I to chase them away and leave them to the wild beasts in the gorges?"

The aldermen nodded their heads. "Very well," they said, "we will support your decision, prince, and out of honor to your great grandmother and our Princess Libuše, we agree."

Thus Hostivít accepted into the Czech lands the people that stood below his window, and the foreign nation long praised him for this. The ruler allowed them to settle near the Prague Castle, and all then swore loyalty to him and help, even in arms, to the land where they had found a new home after long aimless wandering. Their settlement below the castle, where they built a synagogue, soon flourished thanks mainly to their industriousness and thriftiness. The presence of this people below the Prague Castle was noticed some time after the middle of the tenth century by the respected Jewish merchant Ibrahim Ibn Jakub, diplomat in the service of the Califf of Cordoba, Al-Hakam II, during a visit to Prague.

During the reign of Prince Vratislav, who became the first Czech king, there were several times as many Hebrew people in Prague as came originally. Therefore they asked that the prince grant them more space. He allowed them to expand their territory to the right bank of the Vltava and settle near the route between the castles, closer to Vyšehrad which was Vratislav's main seat. Here the Jews began to build a more permanent home. From the original thirty wooden houses soon a sizable town sprang up. A wooden synagogue was added, and here settled families of Hebrews, or Jews. For the most part nobody in the Czech lands knew that they were of a different origin and faith than the other residents. They lived in cohabitation with the natives, and some quickly adopted their customs and manners, but they passed on their unhappy history to succeeding generations. They continued to assemble in their synagogues for worship, helped each other, and lived out their greater and lesser fates together. Many of them truly remained faithful to the old promise to the ruler and the country that had provided them with a home and livelihood.

Evil Times

vil times came at the end of the eleventh
century. In the year 1096 hoards of extremely
fanaticized people rolled across western Europe
and Rhineland and on into central Europe,
destroying what they saw fit to destroy on their
way to the east, and leaving behind a wasteland. They made
themselves out to be pious pilgrims and warriors of the first
"crusade", but these were no knights of Christ. This was
a gang of adventurers, violent and morally depraved, from
the ranks of the lower strata, who wanted to get rich at any
cost. The crowd was assembled from escaped monks and
prisoners, thieves and murderers. They had no scruples and
were not ashamed to use the sign of the cross to assure
themselves freedom from punishment in the future if
someone caught them. At least so the chronicler writes of
them. And in this environment rose up hatred for the Jews,
a raging antisemitism. How could it be otherwise? Where they
sensed wealth, there they headed. The army of "crusaders"
set out under the leadership of Prince Folkmar of France and
grew on its path across Germany to twelve thousand people.
They gained further supporters with a promise of great booty
and the gratitude of God.

In May of 1096 the mob of ragged and violent men passed
through Saxony into Bohemia and Prague. It already had
behind it many murders and much violence. At that time
Prince Břetislav was absent from Prague and could not put

a stop to the fanaticized mob. The "crusaders" hurled
themselves upon the Jews below the Prague Castle, who
were living here peacefully, displaying their goods and sitting
with their families. The mob cleaned out the shops and
stuffed goods that were not theirs into sacks. They put
money in their moneybags and justified their actions as
being in the service of holy baptism. One seized a Jew and
another baptized him by force, laughing the whole while!
And how could it be otherwise, when they continually
imbibed stolen drink. They told of having baptized the Saxon
pagans and killing on the spot those who resisted. Whoever
of the Jews refused baptism and insisted on keeping the
faith of his ancestors was killed. Then the mob headed with
great booty to Moravia and Hungary. Near Nitra in Slovakia,
however, people were waiting for them and stood in their
way. The mob was vanquished. All the same, their booty was
large. They had wreaked great havoc, which they regarded as
an achievement pleasing to God, and planned a similar
campaign for the future.

The crusaders' antisemitism fell on fertile ground in Prague
at the time. Many people reported to the "crusaders" those
who were prospering the most – and they didn't even have to
be Jews. Some Christians were irritated by the fact that the
Jews excelled in business skills, the ability to foresee
conditions, and were so persistent that from collectors of rags
or bones or skins with a sack on their backs they made
themselves into rich craftsmen and merchants, and thus
hatred grew among people. For Jews and Christians are not
simply people virtuous and erring.

When hatred for the Jews in Prague continued to grow,
some took their possessions and moved to Poland or
Moravia, fearing a new pogrom. They sold their homes for
a good price and for the money built themselves better
homes elsewhere. In Hungary, too, lived many Jews and they
prospered there. The departure of the Jews from Prague into

מהר"ר אביגדור ב' א'

אז נגבו האיש המשכיל

שדה ידידים · הלומדתורה ערבים

העם קהדים · בקן היה · מתורה בבל

תבמה ההבמה ונסקד המקרא ומהר

אביגדור קרא בנזה הקצידק קרא ונטירא

פנים היה בעמי · נפטרוהלך לעולמן

בשנתא טאיר ונקף ב'יום ארב צדקהלפקד

צדקרנא ב' ונקף · למען טמיר נסתרה צידים

תהא ונפרה וצרה הנצרה בצרור

neighboring lands, however, hurt the princes' income,
and so in 1098 Prince Břetislav II took firm action. His
chamberlain was given the task of confiscating from the
Jews below the Castle everything of value if they did not
abandon their resettlement fever, and the takings went to
the princely treasury for state purposes. The Jews thus
suffered for the second time, for Břetislav's soldiers took
everything and left the poor Jews only the grain they needed
to live on. The chronicler Kosmas writes that such riches
were not transported even from burned Troy to the shores
of Greece, and another chronicler informs us that the prince
deprived the Jews of "an immense treasure in gold, silver,
and precious stones".

Then came a catastrophe for the Jewish settlement
beneath the Prague Castle when the Přemyslid princes were
struggling for power in the land. In 1142 the settlement
including its synagogue burned down and lay in ashes.
Only then was another Jewish settlement established
on the right bank of the Vltava near the fords, where other
foreign merchants were already living at the time.
This became the Jewish base and center in Bohemia,
the future Prague ghetto.

The Jews in Prague

he Jews did not only stay in Prague's Old Town, where they had their ghetto. They lived scattered about the fringes of Prague. There they built their settlements and little houses, and opened little stores or workshops of all manner. They were good tailors, grocers, delicatessen operators, and textile merchants. They did very well in money exchange and real estate transactions, in sale and purchase of buildings and land. Sometimes so well, it is true, that somebody less honest managed to ruin somebody less clever in the fervor of his work. Jews were often expelled from the over-populated city, where with their stores they became not so much superfluous as rather unwelcome competition. Disputes often arose between Christians and Jews. There were also short periods when they jointly contemplated why they couldn't all live together in peace and contentment, but soon the undeclared truce was foiled again by some Jew or Christian who spat on the honor of one or the other. The guilt was usually on both sides. Expansive ambitions on the part of some, the intolerance of others, feelings of racial superiority, hatred, and fear for one's own bread and place on earth – all this caused continual and endless problems, disputes, and hateful accusations.

The great pogrom during the crusaders' campaign in 1096 was far from the last. In April 1389 another bloody pogrom took place in which three thousand Jews lost their lives, and thievery, fires, and murders were followed by further horrors.

During the reign of the Přemyslids and succeeding rulers, the Jews in Bohemia patiently developed their businesses and their means of earning a living. Often they were better at this than the native Praguers. After their long pilgrimage from their ancient homeland they had in their blood the ability to unite, to defend themselves, to guard what was theirs, and to sense danger from any direction at any time. They knew how to plan ahead and predict future prices and values that declined or rose with all commodities. Whereas the native people rested on their laurels and were often painfully afflicted or ruined by sudden changes, the Jews knew better how to prepare themselves for such blows. They knew how to bargain for good exchanges and purchases, especially of buildings. As representatives and hired managers of property, they usually settled disputes in favor of their clients, and so they soon were able to buy their own land, buildings, forests, and in later centuries even factories.

During the time of the Roman Empire after the violent end of the Jewish national state, Jews became important agents in international trade, and such has been the case up to the present day. In western Europe Jews in many cases even had a privileged position in trade. This was based on their attributes and abilities – on their industriousness, education, and thriftiness. In contrast with other people, Jews were immensely loyal to each other. Solidarity, an attribute that many nations lack altogether, replacing it with envy, facilitated trading for the Jews all over Europe without regard to religious barriers and nationality.

The Jewish Town in Prague was later called by grateful residents "The Mother of Israel". (The Germans liked to say that all Prague was their mother.) There was often unrest in Prague because of continual disputes spawned by the intolerant and the envious. Especially at Easter time, when preachers in the churches spoke of the crucifixion of Christ, the people called out: "The Jews crucified Christ – let them pay for it with their own blood!" Like black ravens, they hurled themselves on unarmed Jews, stoned them, beat them to death, tore the clothes off them, and confiscated their valuables in the manner of the "crusaders". In Jewish cemeteries they knocked down gravestones and opened the graves. Some Jews couldn't stand it and killed their wives, children, and finally themselves so as not to suffer these tortures. Thus they were proclaimed suicides – heathens – and those who survived were afraid to go out from their homes. Therefore they turned to the leader of the whole congregation, to their rabbi, and he in turn to the king. For a while there was peace – days of reconciliation came – until again some intolerant maniac thought up other slanders and incited hatred in the people.

For centuries on the afternoon of Yom Kippur – which means Day of Atonement – a well-known song titled "All This Misery" composed by the Prague rabbi and poet Avigdor Kara about the bloody Easter events in 1389 has been recited and sung in the Old-New Synagogue.

Thus peaceful and stormy times alternated. People and their opinions changed. Little houses in the Jewish ghetto turned into bigger ones. Prague's Jewish Town, though it had long since lost its original form, nevertheless has preserved not a little from earlier times: above all the Old Jewish Cemetery, where ancient gravestones have survived with names of leading figures among the residents of the ghetto at the time. Here you find the grave of the above-mentioned poet Avigdor Kara from 1439, as well as those of Rabbi Löw and his wife and many other important persons.

In the twelfth and thirteenth centuries, a remarkable Jewish settlement developed in Prague, so that a town within a town arose. Out of fear that the Jews would encroach further, the administration of the City of Prague separated

them from the others with stone walls and gates, which were closed at night. Despite this, streets and synagogues were built. Already at the beginning of the twelfth century a "yeshivah" was established here – a school or "Jewish Academy" – and in 1527 a Hebrew printing shop was established. Even before this, in 1512, the "sidur" prayer book was printed in Hebrew. On today's Dušní Street, where the Spanish Synagogue now stands, was the Old Jewish School; over time, prayer rooms and synagogues grew in number.

Not until the arrival of the wise Rabbi Löw, who visited the Emperor Rudolf II at his court in Prague, and the equally important Mordechai Maisel, who lent this ruler money on a regular basis for state and personal purposes, did greater calm and relief come to the Jewish community. Nevertheless for a long time, still in the time of Emperor Charles VI and Maria Theresia, Jews in Bohemia had restricted freedom. Only the oldest son in a family could marry; the others had to move away.

In 1781 it seemed that better times were on the way. Serfdom was abolished and reforms loosened restrictions on the social life of Jews as well, in both civil and religious matters. But not until the reforms after 1848 was it inadmissible to segregate people from others in the ghettos. Jews were no longer marked with their sign and could resettle wherever they wanted. They could devote themselves to work and study without restriction. In 1784 the limited autonomy of the ghetto up to that time in civil and penal jurisdiction was abolished, and everything was taken over by state authorities. German was established as the official language in the Jewish communities, which conformed to requirements for the Czech population at the time. Starting in 1786, however, Jews were also required to take German family names. Some did this, while others resisted. It was at this time that the Jewish family names Klein, Sonnenschein, Hartman, and others originated.

They saved every penny, had their savings associations, and besides leather and hardware products they sold more valuable items. With the development of industry, factory owners summoned educated and clever Jews to manage their factories, just as the nobility before them had called them to their farms – and in this they were not foolish, for the Jews were good at this. Those who lived on the banks of the ever-flooding Vltava soon learned that fire and water were unfriendly elements and persecuted them. Some were surprised – why, water and fire helped Rabbi Löw create the golem. One man dreamed that the golem had indeed come to life and came into the settlement on the Vltava where poor people had their workshops and premises. He told them: "Don't call me. Water and fire are our friends. Just look what all they give you. Do you think without the Vltava you could have your leather tanneries?" And indeed! The Jews needed water and fire in the Old Town and elsewhere where fate allowed them to settle. They gave thanks that at least they could no longer be expelled from the Czech lands, exiled, as almost happened in 1541 and 1744.

Whenever something bad happened in the country it was blamed on the Jews. Once they "caused" an epidemic of plague, another time a fire that raged up to the royal castle, and during the reign of Empress Maria Theresia they were suspected of sympathizing with the Prussian king and the enemy. Therefore it was undesirable that they be left in the lands of their heritage.

Jews found out about these intentions at the time, and it happened that a man came to the chamberlain of Count Leopold Krakovský of Kolovraty to ask whether he could speak with the count. The count guessed immediately what he wanted and told the chamberlain to send him away. So the man left, but after some time he returned. He told the chamberlain that he would give him five ducats if he could say just one word. Just to be allowed into the room.

The chamberlain told everything to the count, who said: "Fine, let him in, but only one word!"

After a while the door opened. The man entered, bowed in silence to the Imperial Court Counsel and Minister Count Krakovský, then said in German: "Schweigen!" ("Be silent!") Then he again bowed respectfully, went out, and gave the chamberlain five ducats.

After some time there was a conference at the court where it was discussed whether the Jews should be expelled or not. Maria Theresia headed the meeting. Count Kounic strongly argued in favor of the Jews. Count Kolovrat only sat in silence. The Empress shook her head; she did not understand this. After a while she asked:

"What are you thinking about, count, that you don't say anything at all?"

And he declared: "I'm pondering how much Count Kounic's chamberlain got for speaking, if mine got five ducats for being silent."

The Jewish Town in Prague is no longer bounded by any wall or any foolish orders and directives. People marry when they like and as they like; many mixed marriages have come about. And there are still whole families of Jews faithful to their race who for generations have adhered to the Hebrew customs and principles. The former Prague ghetto is a large monument to long-past times when the Jews came to love Libuše's city and their wish to settle in it permanently was fulfilled. The old ghetto is a unique conglomeration of Jewish landmarks in central Europe – Gothic, Renaissance, Baroque, and completely new. So it is no wonder that there is unusual interest in it from all corners of the world. The life of this distinctive place has also inspired many Czech artists – for example the sculptor Ladislav Šaloun, who created an art nouveau statue of the famous Rabbi Löw placed on the corner of the New City Hall, and the Czech master František Bílek, whose especially effective statue of Moses adorns the little park by the Old-New Synagogue.

Visitors to the Jewish Town, however, are attracted above all by the legendary golem. Where is he? How did he come into being? Where did he go? Is it possible to see that place? So we shall take you into the time of Rabbi Löw, who created the golem, and to the time of the rich and wise Maisel, to the court of Emperor Rudolf II, who governed over them and made concessions because he knew why this was good for both sides.

Rabbi Löw
and Rudolf II

t that time there was much strife between Prague Christians and the Jews from the ghetto, and various complaints and gossip were brought to Rudolf II. The capricious ruler didn't like putting out needless fires of contention that broke out in the land because of intolerance. He was occupied with more merry fires in the workshops of his alchemists, and he lost his patience. The Jews were allegedly cheating customers in their shops, giving them snow jobs, praising women's hair and legs and at the same time throwing on the scales something they shouldn't. In unguarded moments they would take something from the weighed pile and add it to their own. You throw them out of one door and they stand at the next. They look into windows and ask about everything. They simply have a strange nature, so you can't believe anything they say. Reports even surfaced that the Jews needed the blood of Christians for their ceremonies. If they didn't live here at all it would be better for everybody. But every ruler has explained:

"My dear people, the Jews are good businessmen; they're much better than you! They bring in what can be brought – spices, silk, tobacco, exotic fruits, fabric, and lace. What would it be like here if the Jews didn't bring the goods we want for holidays from their wanderings through the world? You say they cheat? But Christians do, too, and what's more, they think they can then calmly repent of this in confession. What to do with them? Let them be. Their lives are now

grown into the walls of Prague; they have built their homes
here and there and have a synagogue. What to do about all
this? Where are they to go? Home? You see how ignorant you
are, people? They have long been at home all over the world,
because they lost their original country. Have mercy on them
and don't wish them to be grateful to you other than in the
way they show it."

If the ruler looked at it this way, the people should too.
Some understood, while others could not be convinced.
That's the way it was and probably always will be. At such
times the Jews and their wise rabbi understood that it would
be possible to converse with the emperor of king. Löw himself
decided to request an audience at the court. He asked to be
announced in the ruler's chamber because he needed to speak
with him in this difficult time.

Rudolf II was also acquainted with difficult situations and
was glad to turn to the rabbi. The willing Maisel always lent him
money at reasonable interest rates and for things wise as well
as unwise. So what could he do! He invited the clever rabbi to
come on a certain day at a certain time. As soon as the rabbi
found himself in Rudolf's chamber, he took a seat as the
emperor bade and words veritably gushed from him. He
defended his Jews and asked that the ruler no longer allow
such stupid and crass slanders as call to heaven for revenge.
He explained how ridiculous the stories were about making
sacred Jewish bread with Christian blood, what words the
Jewish law contained, and that bloodshed is prohibited to Jews
by law. And nevertheless, word was being spread among the
people of Prague how his people bathed in Christian blood at
their ceremonies.

Rudolf first nodded his head and then declared: "Dear rabbi,
what else could I wish for this land than justice? What else
would I want to defend than the truth? But now answer me
a question that often remains open among Christians. Are Jews
guilty of the crucifixion of Christ? And don't you think that this

feud between Christians and Jews goes back to the time of Christ? How will you answer this?"

The rabbi bowed: "Your highness, I will answer with an allegory, as your people like. One powerful king had a son and the son had many enemies. The son revealed his enemies' unfair business practices and with his young sharp eyes followed their actions; he read their minds. But the father was weary from old age and believed his corrupt advisors, who were doing well for themselves with the weak king. Some things he didn't notice, others he forgave. But the son would certainly rule firmly and uncover evil deeds. Therefore a slander was needed. They slandered the son to his father, saying he was impatient to ascend to the throne and was plotting a coup against his own father. The king, who loved his son immensely, was crushed. But he believed false witnesses and summoned his son to give him the chance to explain everything. The son looked at his father and gazed into his eyes in silence. He did not defend himself. Perhaps the father would snap out of his confusion – perhaps he would recognize the falsity of the accusations he was making against his son. The distrust from the mouth of his father overwhelmed him. The father frowned. The son was not defending himself; he was silent because the nail had been hit on the head.

"You don't speak. Very well. I understand that you are ashamed, my son. So I will place you before a court. But there you will speak."

He placed his son before a court. How he wanted to speak, how he wanted to defend himself! But he looked around himself, and what did he see? Most of the witnesses, even the judge, were his enemies. So he closed his lips firmly and remained silent.

So they condemned the king's son to death, and when the executioner stood over the poor man, for the first time the son turned his innocent eyes to his father:

"Father, my father, surely you won't let your own son die, will you?"

But the king remained resolute even at this moment and preferred to raise his hand quickly as a sign that the execution be carried out.

The rabbi fell silent and then said: "That is all. Perhaps it is enough for you to understand."

Rudolf, in confusion, began cleaning his ring with his lace handkerchief, and so the rabbi helped him. "Whose fault was it that this young heir to the throne was deprived of his life? This innocent son of his father the king. Was the judge who made the decision guilty, or the king, he who stood over all, several levels closer to heaven?"

Rudolf nodded his head, patted the rabbi on his shoulder, and said: "Go home to your people, rabbi. I will help you. I will summon a man who is still closer to heaven. With his wisdom and strange instruments, by which he joins himself to the shining of the stars, he reaches the stars and communicates with them. No, he is not any ordinary jester or magician. He came from Denmark. The sea brought him to us and the wind showed him the way from the reefs on the shore. He, too, made enemies in one country and so sought another. Just as many foreigners who abandon their country or their world like it here, so he too liked Bohemia and made his home here. He is the famous astronomer Tycho de Brahe, a nobleman who even left behind his own castle far beyond the frontiers. He passed through many countrysides and met many people, but wants to find his final resting place here. Yes, I promised it to him, in the Týn Church on the Old Town Square, in the middle of the city of Prague. There he can one day rest. A Czech princess, they say, once prophesied that the glory of this city would reach to the stars. Wouldn't this be the right place for an astronomer?"

And Rudolf II, he who knew well the fickleness of fate, declared further: "I, too, have many enemies, rabbi, wherever

I look. Why, I can't even believe my own brother. He is betraying me and striving to gain my throne. I, too, have many opponents and fewer of those who are favorably inclined toward me. My enemies are opposing me at the court in Vienna, at the Prague Castle, and in Hungary. I am betrayed by the nobility and the people, and by the lovers I embrace." After a while the emperor sighed: "But it is time for us to finish this talk together." Rudolf rang the bell and the servant received the order to quickly call the astronomer into the receiving hall. Before a leaf could fall from a tree, Tycho de Brahe appeared.

The king introduced the two men and said: "All sorts of people in Bohemia are complaining about the Jewish people. All sorts of people tell me the most varied stories and bring abominable tidings. Here is Rabbi Löw, who is the highest of them, trying to prove to me with words and explanations of Jewish law that none of this is true. It is up to you, celebrated man, to help us confirm via the stars where the truth stands among them."

Tycho de Brahe smiled, nodded his head, scratched his beard, and promised to do so.

The Wise Tycho de Brahe

everal weeks passed. Rabbi Löw was beginning to doubt that Rudolf would keep his promise. He had heard many stories about this king, of which only some were completely true and many remained merely gossip. Yes, he was a hedonistic ruler. He liked to be surrounded by women, wine, good roasts, and a truly royal life. He wanted to smell of lilies and orange blossoms in citrus orchards, to shine with gold on his clothing and shoes, and for his splendidly gilded chambers to be full of the most varied marvels – statuary, playing clocks and porcelain dancing dolls. He loved lions so much that after one died he became ill from grief. He didn't eat and didn't sleep, and that was something to see! They laughed at him. But even an emperor has a heart. One day, when they performed his autopsy, they would see that heart and a Czech nobleman would throw it on the table in rage. But all this was written in the stars.

Yes, Rudolf II was capricious and moody. Extravagant. On the other hand he allowed himself to be fooled by charlatans of all manner, and they did well for themselves at the court until their frauds burst open. The nobility rebuked him that he did not care enough about dignity, and the people, that he allowed himself to be controlled by the nobility. He didn't win anybody's gratitude. Moody he was, yes. He suffered from gout. And then – wasn't this whole period one knot of moods in Europe? Among such ponderings and anxieties it was no wonder that it was often faith in magical powers that kept him alive – faith in the positions of the stars and fates.

Tycho de Brahe finally responded to the emperor, who summoned the rabbi on that day. The famous astronomer declared at the Prague Castle that day:

"Between the Jewish and Christian people in Prague there are often persecutions and quarrels, which always arouse necessary opposition and response from the other side. It is not good to do this on either side. Christians and Jews each have their Almighty and honor his laws. To honor the law of one's ruler and believe in his power and truth leads the people to virtue. One of the most important principles is to honor the highest creator in each person, because all were created in God's image. This does not mean that he who does not please me because he has a different color of skin or eyes, sings different songs, or speaks in different words is not worthy of human love and the attention of the world. All rose up from one earth and above them arose stardust or shone the sun on the day of their birth. All are sons or daughters of one mother earth. Therefore no one has the right to wreak violence on another because of various differences or to ridicule him or even persecute him.

"Those who came to this land as guests, but remained here among brothers with their permission, should live their lives in their conditions in order not to draw too much attention to themselves, and in no case should they ever wish to dominate or oppress their hosts. They must thank God with their lips that they found a home here and brothers and sisters; though they are stepbrothers and stepsisters, they are nevertheless from a single human family. For a sin that one of them commits the whole race and whole nation may not be punished, but only the guilty one, whatever his color or language. For all manner of guilty parties there is in every country a court."

"Fine," said the emperor, "let it be so for the future. If a Christian has anything against a Jew and vice versa, a proper court will always be called. No private wrong or personal punishment will be handled without a court. If a Jewish citizen

causes any evil, the whole Jewish community will not be
punished for it. And you, rabbi, as the representative of your
people, will participate in every court."

The rabbi kneeled before the king and thanked him, bowed
to the astronomer with great respect, and went to tell his people
of the meeting at the royal throne and the whole content of the
words of the distinguished men.

When the rabbi had left, Tycho de Brahe declared
thoughtfully after a while:

"These same stars shall witness human times far in the
future, when we, dear emperor, are not here. On your throne
the velvet will be worn through a thousand times, your ermine
devoured by whole generations of moths. Court judges will be
changed a hundred times, but the justice they decree over the
centuries will be just as unstable. Centuries will pass,
generations will be laid in their cemeteries, and new mothers
will bear new sons and daughters. But believe me, emperor,
man will always remain only man and will be intolerant, full
of ill will and hatred and needless longing for material things.
He will trade his soul for them, his honor and love; he will
exchange all the lasting beauties of human life for money and
vain things. A new Redeemer would have to come to earth,
brought perhaps by the fairies of the deep forests.

"And what about the Jewish people? Scattered about all
countries of the world, they will continually strive as they strive
today, as a green sprout strives to grow toward the sun in a dark
crevice. If they are wise and quick to learn, they will achieve
good positions in trade, in art, and everywhere where they can
excel above others, where they can draw attention to themselves.
However, not all of them will do well. As with Christians, not
everyone has a word in the stars, an advocate with the sun, so it
will be here too. Also, some will violate the law of the heart. They
will not honor the Jewish law. Others will envy each other. But for
the most part they will extend their hands to each other even
across the sea. They will help each other, because they will have

enough envy from the ranks of the Christians, even though the Holy Bible forbids it to them. They will envy the success of the Jews and seek faults in them even where there are none, using them as an excuse to hold the reigns on them like on a wild horse, pulling them back in the mouth. Woah!

"And for this reason I remained silent to the rabbi on only one matter, dear emperor: the forecast of long-lasting persecution. Such persecution as can be perpetrated only by man without respect for man, his brother on this planet. And there will be evil and bloody times. Every Jewish son and daughter will be marked with a yellow star on his or her clothing, so that all in the ranks of the mercenaries of death can easily recognize them. There will be a hunt after Jews in all of Europe, just as a short time from now in Bohemia and neighboring lands there will be a hunt for witches, those poor wise women to whom nature has been kind."

The emperor did not even breathe. He listened to the famous astronomer and astrologer who understood the stars as he understood his own heart. This man preferred to immerse himself in the scientific laws of the paths of the stars, because from the images the stars showed him as a forecast of the future his head and soul hurt. How much evil was projected here, and how much trampled virtue, striving, and hope!

The Apparition of Father Abraham

udolf was pleased by every conversation with the rabbi and by what he heard about him. This was the very thing he liked, for which he longed: magic, tricks, and miracles. How much the rabbi told of this! Who would believe it all?

The rabbi said he had been walking early one morning on the Stone Bridge, which Charles IV had ordered built long ago, and some juvenile delinquents, probably incited by adults of course, began throwing stones at his head. Whoever knocked off the cap that adorned the rabbi's head, it would be his. The reason? What right did he have to walk on a bridge that belonged to the Christians? Isn't that an insult in and of itself? These Prague street urchins acted according to the proverb, "Whoever wants to beat a dog will find a stick."

And behold! The rabbi bent over to pick up a stone that had struck him in the forehead – and instead of a stone he picked up flowers. And he wasn't wounded at all! A servant girl from the bakery by the bridge tower saw this and spread the news through the Lesser Side and the Old Town. In a short while the story was being told all over Prague and made its way even to the royal castle.

There must be something magical about this rabbi, Emperor Rudolf said to himself, and he wanted to test the holiness of this man. Why not? They already knew each other: they had conversed together several times in the Castle by now. It was worth a try. Rudolf pondered how to test the rabbi, and then it occurred to him: let the rabbi invite the ghosts of his ancestors to the Castle! One evening he sent word to the rabbi to come to him. He drank mead and Viennese beer for courage and then, bored and intoxicated by the alcohol, declared as soon as he had fallen into his chair: "Be seated, rabbi, man of the Jewish race, I have heard that you are capable of transformations. Miracles. My jesters repeat the same tricks over and over and I have an appetite to see something strange and new. So show me what you can do. I have helped you, too," Rudolf didn't forget to add.

The rabbi stood humbly before him and waited to find out what the drunken ruler would think up for him.

"So it occurred to us, dear rabbi, to invite into our company the great great great... but you know how many times great – grandfathers Abraham, Isaac, Jacob, and his sons."

The rabbi said nothing. He hesitated. He saw that it was a serious situation and that he must not let himself be taken by surprise. Who could say what mood the ruler had today from among his whole palette? And it was impossible to resist him in this condition. Therefore he shifted from one foot to the other, coughed, and then slowly uttered: "It is really a very unusual wish and at the moment I don't know how to fulfil it. Perhaps the emperor could wait a few days. There must be calm and deliberation for everything. It's not possible immediately. It will take a lot of effort." The rabbi thought that in the meantime the ruler's whim would pass or that in drunkenness he would forget what he had said a while earlier. But no way! The rabbi received a merciful delay of three days and then the royal carriage would come for him.

What was he to do? At this time there was a certain alchemist at Rudolf's court – the rabbi's neighbor. That evening the rabbi went to him for advice. They put their heads together and to their own amazement, a ceremonious presentation occurred to them which all of Prague certainly remembered for a long time in the Rudolfinian era.

The guests were invited. Beside themselves with curiosity, they pressed in front of each other to get a better view. They made a tremendous clamor with chairs until Rabbi Löw finally appeared: "Shall we begin?" He called upon all those present, saying that above all it was necessary to preserve quiet and darkness. After all, only in the dark and in deep silence do unusual things happen, apparitions appear, and miracles take place.

So the servants extinguished all the lanterns and absolute darkness set in. Rabbi Löw began praying out loud in Hebrew and in the quiet his voice rose all the way to the vaulted ceiling of the hall. And what did the learned Rabbi Löw pray for, what did he ask?

"Our distant ancestor, celebrated Abraham, I implore you to appear before these people, above all before their Emperor Rudolf, who asks for you. Hear my fervent prayers and convince those present here that you existed and remain for our people the force that protects it from weakness. I also ask you, Isaac, Jacob, and Jacob's sons, our ancient ancestors, appear to us, we implore!"

Such a silence fell over the hall that a feather would be heard if a lost pigeon dropped it on the window sill. And in this darkness and in this silence all at once a warm breeze arose and with it came floating a little white cloud that veiled a blue figure, passing quickly but in a dignified way among the guests. "It is he," one woman already wanted to whisper, but she was too overwhelmed even to speak. But the others, too, recognized father Abraham in the figure. And after him came the others whom the king and emperor Rudolf had wished to see. Isaac, Jacob, and Jacob's sons passed through with a dignified stride. However, when they saw the last son of Jacob, named Naftali, jump about squirmingly in the bluish cloud, the emperor couldn't stand the tension and broke out laughing. This gave the sign for general relaxation and the hall filled with laughter.

At that moment all was lost and dissolved, and the show was over. Some grumbled about the crass and crude among the audience, and others shared their feelings, but in any case it was the end of the scene. Only to the servants did it seem that the ceiling of the hall somehow trembled and moved. Then, when the lighted lanterns again illuminated the room, all the others as well asserted this. They said the ceiling was definitely lower, because the cloud from heaven had evidently brought in the apparition by that route.

The Rabbi's Sholet

For a long time people at the Prague court and even in Vienna talked about what had happened here. Some held the rabbi to be a dangerous wizard. Others asserted that this was one of the tricks that surrounded Rudolf II in Prague wherever one looked. Who knows? The rabbi made it clearly known that he was not and would not be a court entertainer and in no case planned to repeat similar tricks. Rudolf II took this seriously. From that time on the Prague people, too – including most Christians – respected the rabbi and his teachings. It seemed that a better day was dawning for the Jewish community.

However, so that Rudolf II could get to know the environment of the Jewish leader, the rabbi invited him to his home. Emperor Rudolf never went to any unknown venues alone, so of course he took his entourage with him. Rabbi Löw led the distinguished guests into his home, small at first glance. Inside he had delicacies prepared for all, the most select foods such as this court had never tasted.

Rudolf II sat down at the head of the table. Before him they placed a silver platter of "sholet". It was peas mixed with boiled barley and buttered with goose fat. Under the peas lay goose livers steamed in wine, and on top of the pile of sholet blushed a whole quarter of a goose including the "parson's nose" (the portion of meat at the tail bone). The rabbi shouldn't have called the "parson's nose" by this expression, however, because the emperor's adjutant frowned at this. But Rudolf observed, "An accurate description – our parson is so fat he could hardly pass through the alleys of Vienna if he didn't ride in a carriage."

All of this was to be accompanied by good wine. One lady got up her courage and cautiously tasted this dish, dabbling at the peas, then again barley. She swallowed cautiously, then quickly helped herself again and again – but not with a fork! She went for the big spoon, so as not to dabble herself to death. So she began to develop a taste for that sholet. Then the others around the table joined in one after the other, and so the food gradually disappeared from the golden and silver bowls and platters. A joy to behold.

When everything had been eaten up and drunk, the rabbi clapped his hands – and as a desert came a cake, accompanied by Hebrew music. Black-haired dancers moved in graceful waves to it, and one in particular pleased Rudolf. Thank goodness he glanced in time at his ladies from the court – with one of them there he had an unfinished affair – and so he declared: "Dear rabbi, everything the human body needs I have found in your home, but now I have had enough of these temptations. However, I would be glad if you would have the recipe for this good food that I've just sampled in your home written down for me. I'll give it to the royal cooks in the Castle when I want to liven up the menu. They often complain that they don't know what to prepare for me any more."

"Fine," the rabbi smiled, and called his waiter. A young man still without whiskers ran up smiling, bowed to the head of the Czech lands, and listened to his master's wish. Then he brought a pen and paper and set to writing. Meanwhile he repeated everything so that nothing would be forgotten. In the meantime the rabbi mentioned that Levi ben Gershom of Bagnoles, a Jewish scholar, mathematician, and astronomer who was born in 1288 and died in 1344, had enjoyed sholet long ago. This scientist and inventor of navigating instruments, author of many works, allegedly prepared the dish himself because in his hours of scholarship, of endless pondering, he couldn't stand gabby women. So he himself prepared half a kilogram of peas – he liked yellow ones the best – and in another pot he boiled half a kilogram of large barley grains. Then he mixed the two ingredients in a larger vessel and sauteed onions in goose fat separately. Of course this was in the autumn, when nicely yellow fatty geese were available in the markets. He bought one such goose, baked it, and cut it into manageable portions. He placed the portions on a platter and covered them with the peas and barley, sprinkled on the sauteed onions, and as a side dish added sauerkraut.

So the recipe was written and handed over to the emperor, whose mouth was already watering, and the rabbi sent the young waiter back where he had come from. He was to think of some other recipe and write it down for the emperor as well. So the rabbi proclaimed wisely, looking at the emperor with a calm gesture of the hand:

"Now let your soul receive something as well, now that the body is sated." He put a finger to his lips so that they wouldn't interrupt the beautiful concert. The emperor himself survived it, so the courtiers and distinguished guests showed their approval too. Some applauded and wanted an encore, but they were in the minority, and what's more, Rudolf, as was his habit, needed to doze off after a good meal. This he could do well only at home, and therefore he bade his farewell to the excellent hosts with thanks.

In taking his leave he turned to the rabbi with one more request: "I would be glad to actually learn something about your race, about the nation of Israel, of the Jews, about a people that has no country. Can you tell me its history?" The rabbi more than willingly promised to do so. Why, it was important that everyone who wants to decide about somebody or something should obtain all the necessary information.

"Gladly, lord of this land," the rabbi bowed to Rudolf, "but for that it is necessary to withdraw from your merry entourage. Most suitable would be my study." It hadn't occurred to the emperor that the rabbi would comply with his wish immediately. At this he fidgeted, but didn't say a word and followed Löw into another chamber. Meanwhile his companions poured themselves drinks such that the God, father and son of the Christians and the highest of the highest of the Jewish race were scandalized alike.

Meanwhile the rabbi sat the distinguished guest in a splendid armchair adorned with gold. For himself he took an ordinary chair on which he sat at his desk when he was preparing sermons and meditations. And he began to tell the history of the Jewish people as passed from mouth to mouth among this race of wise and hard-working people.

Rabbi Löw
on the
Semite Nation

he Semitic nation, the Israelites, the Hebrews – so they are variously called – once had their own land. Originally they lived in southern Canaan and on the steppes to the east of the broad river Jordan. As legend has it, the Israelites moved away in times of hunger and famine to the land of Goshen in lower Egypt, from which Moses led them out. They didn't arrive in Canaan until after his death. Then it took a long time before the various Israeli tribes finally settled in various places in their "new Promised Land". Of course this couldn't be done without battles with the Canaan kings. Nevertheless, they did not have a unified state. They still lived as a commonwealth in tribes, under the rule of their "elders", i. e. wise men or patriarchs. Before them certain chosen "judges" ruled their tribes, experienced and clever people who judged trespasses and counseled in case of feuds. But they longed to have a king as nations did elsewhere.

The first King of Israel was Saul, whose adjutant or counselor was Samuel the prophet. The reign of the first king was again marked by battles with neighbors, mainly with the Philistines, and outstanding in the battles at the time was David, with his extraordinary intelligence. After the death of Saul, David became king and united the Israeli tribes into a single whole. Jerusalem, well-fortified, became the capital city, and the center of culture, religion, and politics. It even had a royal palace and splendid structures of various sorts.

David's son Solomon later saw to the construction of Jerusalem palaces in appropriate splendor. He adorned the city with all available richness and beauty. His main deed was construction of a temple in honor of the Lord. Solomon himself was a wise man and author of many books. On the other hand, toward the end of his reign began a decline in the political power of the king.

After Solomon's death the empire broke into two Israeli kingdoms – the smaller kingdom of Judah in the south and the Israeli kingdom in the north. In the Judean part reigned the dynasty of David, and on the Israeli throne rulers from various families alternated through the last great Israeli ruler, Jeroboam II.

The two states were often ravaged by fratricidal wars. The Egyptian king stood behind the Israelis, while the Judeans were helped by the Arameans. The policies of domestic "prophets" placed on the throne of the northern kingdom the cruel Jehu, whose dynasty persisted on the throne for a rather long time. The people did not fare very well in these times, in a land threatened by ceaseless battles.

The last great king of Israel of this dynasty – Jeroboam III – was only a flickering light in this long period. He defeated the Arameans and improved his land in all fields. His successors, however, took the path of crabs. They became more and more greatly and more closely dependent on Assyria, until the Assyrian King Shalmaneser II took over Canaan and overthrew the Israeli dynasty. All the subsequent uprisings, supported by Egypt, came to nothing. Samaria was conquered and the best of the Israeli people were killed or taken off by the Assyrians into captivity.

The Judean kingdom still existed, having for the time being avoided a similar fate, and thus it became the guardian and support of Hebrew traditions. However, when King Hezekiah ascended the throne and after him his son, they led the people into the complete slavery that the dependence on Assyria had been, in both politics and religion.

During the reign of King Josiah, when a great decline of the kingdom set in, the religious orders were renewed, to be sure, but under the next king, Jehoiakim, the land succumbed to the Babylonian King Nebuchadnezzar and the Israeli ruler and ten thousand men were exiled to Babylon. Here Zedekiah became king, and as legend has it he was responsible for the complete ruin of the kingdom by an unfortunate accident. Many Israeli families were led off into confinement, some were murdered, and others scattered and fled into the wilderness where they died of hunger or other misfortunes.

Jerusalem was conquered and thus also – in the year 586 – ends the history of the Israelites and their states. It is a sad story and a sad end for this people. Since that time the historical mission of the ancient ancestors has been taken on by their descendants. Surprisingly, it was quite ordinary Jews who suffered the most.

And so they strove and rose again, and again battled and helped each other, even across the sea and across boundaries – and Christians occasionally rebuke them for this.

They remained Jews, with the Hebrew language, the semitic alphabet, Hebrew music, and their scriptures. Legends, myths, and fables. And blood that can never be denied. This was received by the Israeli nation as a birth gift from its Almighty, or the common Almighty: I don't know – after all, the original mother of Christians and Jews was Eve!

Rudolf II listened to the rabbi's captivating narrative with interest and was truly glad that he was informed, and thus could hear in a different way those strange reports that now here, now there the Jews...

The Lesson
with the Fish

Emperor Rudolf, however, was truly a moody man. For a long time after this lecture and after all preceding and following events it seemed that the Jews had won their case with him. But not at all! All it took was some quarrel, dispute, discrepancy, or complaint, and his gall bladder went bad and all lightning and thunder fell on the Jews, who did nothing but evil everywhere.

Soon the rabbi found out that, on the advice of his adjutants, the emperor had even decided to issue a proclamation by which he would finally chase out of his empire all Jews to the last one, mainly from Czech Prague. Here the wheat was blooming for them and even made itself into bread. Who could be expected to endure gall bladder, gout, and the Jewish issue to boot?! It was eternal and would remain eternal, as after all even his astronomer had declared. So let them leave Bohemia and go their own way! Only – here the emperor hesitated – what way of their own? In Bohemia they already had their streets, houses, and synagogues, and they would certainly resist. Perhaps he could consult with the world and give them somewhere a piece of land not belonging to anyone. It was enough for the astronomer to look at some planet not yet inhabited – so pondered the angry emperor and king and already planned how he would chase the Jews out of Bohemia like moths from the ermine of his robe.

He summoned the astronomer once more and asked him whether to expel or not to expel. The astronomer cautiously promised to consult the stars. Some weeks later he came to the emperor and upon his order wisely spoke as follows:

"My Lord, do not expel those who seek protection at your feet. You will be meritorious in the eyes of your God for protecting your fellow men. But don't allow them more than you allow and provide to Christians. All together need your protection, but also above all a firm hand. Have both sides examined once more and strengthen the laws. You say give them a land? It is written in the stars that this too will one day come about. After cruelties and floods of human blood, the God of all humanity, who is one – and let nobody from either side quarrel over his name – will send special wisdom to the heads of nations. Wisdom and mercy shall thus be victorious and the Jewish people will be granted a country."

"And where now is that land of nobody?" Rudolf was interested.

"Its name is veiled in the mists and the stars. But I saw again blood and more blood thereabouts. Because no human, whether Jew or Christian, is ever satisfied with that which is allotted to him. He will want more and will spread out until he comes into boundary disputes and wars. And much wisdom and the work of rabbis of new times will again be needed, and with them also of Christian rulers who must join in word and in love with their neighbor in order to jointly lead the people on the right path of modesty. Only then will agreement be possible. Not every Jew, however, will return to that promised land. Many of them will fuse with various nations and found their families there, and so they will not want to leave their property. Some, again, will grasp the fundamental beneath the superfluous. Because no religion other than that of Satan can declare the rule of gold over the human soul and none will wish to bow again before the golden calf. Otherwise humanity would experience a new Atlantis."

"The stars are wiser than the kings of the world," admitted the emperor, and it seemed that he was sorry about that.

"Emperor, do you know that dissatisfaction, that envy, and that longing to have more than another? Have you understood what I wanted to tell you?" asked the astronomer.

"Yes," Rudolf nodded his head. The astronomer only shrugged his shoulders.

Within the next few days the astronomer Tycho de Brahe dined at a feast to celebrate the birthday of the emperor's adjutant. It was a "small supper" in the little imperial tavern where the ruler used to go to avoid the attention of the court when he wanted to have peace, comfort, and a little diversion. The rabbi was invited too. Everybody could order whatever he had an appetite for; the innkeeper, in holiday garb, had prepared only holiday dishes. Among them were fishes prepared in various ways. The three men – the emperor, the astronomer, and the rabbi – agreed on what they would have. The astronomer did not eat fish, so ordered roast beef, whereas the emperor and the rabbi agreed on fish.

"But I only have one last double portion, prepared with precious spices on a silver platter," reported the innkeeper. "I'll bring it with two plates; you can share then."

The emperor winced a little – why should he share a dish with some rabbi? But the rabbi assured him: "You heard, respected king, distinguished emperor, that the food will be brought on a platter with two plates."

The king and emperor calmed down a little. Two beautiful plates lay before them and in the middle of the table a silver platter. On it were two baked fish. They smelled good and were garnished with pineapple and cherries. But there was a big problem – one was larger and the other smaller.

Both men received silverware on a silk napkin and prepared for the supper. Their nostrils danced like dragonflies over a pond. The men savored the aroma, which opened all the pores in their bodies, and their mouths watered. The rabbi waited. The emperor looked at him. Nothing.

"So help yourself, rabbi," he nudged his table mate. The latter, however, declared:

"Why, that's impossible; after all the king is the one who has priority!"

Rudolf II, however, said graciously: "Your emperor and lord permits you to be the first to take his fish."

The rabbi gazed at the platter. They were nestled against each other, one larger, one smaller. For a while he hesitated, then he reached for the larger one. With refined taste and the conduct of one experienced in table manners he tossed the fish on the plate and waited for Rudolf to do the same after him. For a moment the emperor sat as though he had suffered a blow, and he then cried out agitatedly: "So you see, rabbi, it's true that you Jews are miserly and selfish, that you set out the world for yourselves as on a dining table and reach for the better morsels. This is a true example of the difference between us."

The rabbi wished the king bon appetit, and the emperor, whose appetite was now intense, served himself the smaller fish on his plate. Only then did the rabbi reply calmly to the emperor: "My dearest lord, distinguished ruler, what evil have I done? On the platter were two fish, one for each of us. So I took one."

"Yes," cried Rudolf, "but the larger one."

The rabbi smiled. "May I ask the most distinguished ruler, which of the two fish you would have taken if you had reached toward the platter first?"

"The smaller one, of course!" snapped the agitated emperor.

The rabbi shook his head as though he were speaking with a small child. "Well, then, and what happened differently? You have it on your plate, so what are you complaining about, sir?"

Rudolf II banged on the table and said like a defeated soldier who doesn't like to admit defeat: "Yes, you are the clever ones, you Jews, yes, very clever people, that's a fact."

The rabbi agreed with this: "Most distinguished ruler, be glad that you have clever people as well around you, my lord. There are plenty of idiots around the throne in every kingdom!"

This had to be admitted even by the emperor and king. Because the fish was indeed tasty, he wiped his fat Habsburg lips with his napkin and ordered that another fish be caught quickly in the Vltava. And this one he didn't want to share with anybody. The head cook got the task of finding out how the fish was prepared.

"Carp Jewish style?" smiled the emperor's personal cook. "Why, that's no art! A carp well-washed with the largest bones removed is cut into portions, which I salt and rub lightly with garlic. I dip them lightly in flour and then cook in hot fat, turn them over, continue cooking, and then serve them on a plate – preferably on tin, of course. According to taste I then only add onion cut in strips, and pre-cooked strips of bacon. In a pan I make a white sauce from a piece of butter and flour, thin it with three spoons of tepid water, and let it boil just a little. I pour it over the fish and can serve it to the emperor. Bon appetit!"

The Birth
of the Golem

E ven though the Jews in Prague strove with all their might to see that trade blossomed around them and that everything their customers' hearts desired was always available on the market and pleased them and satisfied their expectations, they never won the gratitude they would have liked to. And yet before their arrival in Bohemia there was not such a wide assortment of goods! Instead of thanks they often harvested only grimaces and what's more – slanders about them spread anew around Rudolf's throne so powerfully and the pressure so mounted that he truly sometimes planned to accommodate the requests of the majority of the inhabitants of the land and rid himself of the endless disputes, suits, and merely temporary solutions, even if it would be at a quite high cost to him and mainly to the Jewish people. He wanted to have peace and time for his hobbies.

The rabbi was unhappy about the change in Rudolf's conduct and recognized that if endless strife ruled on earth it was necessary to have someone besides a rabbi, a king and emperor, and a Lord in heaven. The scholar pondered and decided that he would create a giant from clay. No Adam who would follow the example of Eve and bring misfortune to mankind, but a proper, big giant that all would fear. Where there is fear comes obedience and humility and an end to evil attacks. He invented a golem that could be brought to life with a formula (the shem) placed into a head without reason. The golem would do only that which others ordered him to do. He would belong to the rabbi and his wife, and nobody else would possess the shem; nobody would have the right to bring the golem to life for any deed.

In form the giant would resemble a human. The rabbi would make him from the matter from which humans too were created. He would have to be brought to life with the help of fire and water, the fundamental elements needed for the life of everything on earth. And why not? After all, the astronomer Tycho de Brahe allegedly had read from the stars one evening that people would bring to life matter that would fly in the air, ride around the land, and swim in water. If fish could swim, and fowl, butterflies, and bees could fly, then why shouldn't a human manage to do something similar?

So Rabbi Löw summoned two men for a council. They were clever young people, capable of listening to the wise Maharal without talking back and with great attention and respect. One was his favorite and most dedicated pupil and the other his son-in-law. They put their heads together and pondered how they could harness fire and water, these elements, in such a way that they could bind them into a body of clay. They all agreed that this could be done only through prayer, with the help of a higher force. They trusted the Lord that he would lend them such power and strength, and therefore persisted in prayers for several hours with heads deeply bowed. They fasted and didn't drink, because they knew that where the stomach is full the head is empty and the heart grows over with fat. In their abstention they were guided by the thought of creating somebody or something from which fear would emanate on earth that day. Because people rarely fear that which is to be a punishment tomorrow or after death.

So they prayed continuously and alternated in singing psalms, bowed, and walked seven times around the prepared matter from which was to arise the clay man with the capability of motion and manly strength, nay the strength of several men, and also with obedience. Toward dawn, when the sun was slowly

groping through the mists, they ceased their preparations and lay down to rest for the next day.

On the next day they set to forming the figure of the giant. It took a long time before he had arms and legs, a smooth back, a neck, a head, and strong shoulders. As soon as the giant was ready, they marked ears, eyes, a nose, and a mouth on his head. When they had done so, they watched the giant lying calmly on his back and then they lay down beside him. The next day was designated for filling the matter with heat such that steam would emerge from the giant. Then the rabbi walked around the golem seven times, and finally he placed into his mouth the shem with the secret script.

All three men then bowed to the new unknown who had come into the world, who had fire in his eyes and heat in his body. They looked with amazement at the work that had emerged from their hands and from the will of the Lord. They couldn't believe their eyes, like when an artistic master cannot believe it when he creates a sublime statue.

The golem lived. He stood there in all his power, a helper destined to protect and help the oppressed. The Prague people were afraid of spooks, headless knights, and flying dragons, as is well known. Why couldn't the golem be added to them! The golem would be the Jewish monster, born in Prague. The giant came to life and saw a strange world, and figures so much smaller than he was. He looked down at them and was suddenly aware of his strength. He soon recognized that these people, otherwise more perfect, expected from him – the oaf – precisely that strength, against their fellow citizens.

"Rise, golem, and be at our service. Be a guard against injustice and the violence of others. People are not afraid of anything when they slander us and destroy our lives, which are shorter than a single breath of a star. Some Christians assert that they fear God, but this is not the case. They pray, to be sure, but they sin against Moses's commandments. God will not come to earth no matter how much they pray. God is sitting in heaven, and took with him the Redeemer Jesus Christ, who sits at his right hand there above. But what is needed is to establish order here on earth already today. Allegedly he will come to judge the quick and the dead, but when, when? So we have erected the golem. He is created of clay like a man and he will protect us."

The golem arose and was big, and his eyes glowed. They put clothing on him, and if he knew how to talk, he would certainly have greeted them and asked for breakfast. But not even the Lord in heaven, nor Rabbi Löw on earth, had decreed that he would be able to speak. Therefore he was only to listen and obey. This he knew how to do, and immediately they tried this out.

They gave him the name Josef and a place near the rabbi and his family. The rabbi told his wife: "I'm bringing you a boarder. He will be our servant and protector. He will bring you water, wood, fish, and everything you need for the kitchen. He is mute but obedient."

All the people soon grew accustomed to the golem and preferred to comply with him – they stayed out of his way. They read what they were to place in his basket or bag. The strong golem could lift a lot and carry a lot. At first there were plenty of horrifying or on the contrary humorous episodes with him, until they learned how to handle him and what he was capable of.

The Golem Aids Justice

I t happened, for example, that a certain Jewish girl slandered those who shared her own religion in order to win favor with the Christians. She fell in love with one of them and wanted to convert to the faith of her beloved. To make sure nobody could prevent her, she committed perjury. She asserted that it was not slander but the real truth that Jews drink the blood of Christians. She said she saw it with her own eyes when they killed a girl destined for the sacrifice, a servant from the building where she lived. The servant girl was indeed lost – she had gone out one day and hadn't come back.

Rabbi Löw was saddened by this girl's betrayal of her own people and gave the golem an important task: to search Bohemia for the girl and give her a letter in which the rabbi wrote why it was necessary that she return. In the meantime a court had been appointed and the rabbi was to testify what had happened with that sacrificed girl. He waited impatiently for the golem, but for a long time he did not return. The rabbi and others from the congregation prayed that the golem would bring a real live witness who would refute the shocking slander, and that justice would be victorious. He consoled the frightened people, for on them fell the shame of the slander that came from the mouth of a Jewish girl.

The court was already commenced but the golem had not yet returned. The false witness, in answer to the question of whether she recognized the ones that spilled the blood of the servant girl and drank it in their ceremony, pointed to Rabbi Löw and his assistants. To them she added also servants, and declared:

"One was named Abraham and another Josef – an enormous, strange fellow. He boasted that he liked the taste of that blood."

"But the golem Josef can't talk. How could he boast that he did this?" objected the rabbi. Just then he heard the screech of a carriage before the building of the court and from it lumbered out the golem. He was leading the servant girl by the hand, having found her far away in the countryside.

"So here is the one who boasted and cannot speak – and here is the girl whose blood we Jews drank at the ceremony," said the trembling Rabbi Löw.

The court ended and the golem had thus helped his people for the first time. But he was created precisely for this purpose. From that time on people feared him more, but they appreciated him more, too. And they weighed their words more, too, because the golem, who couldn't speak, made his displeasure known by force instead of words. It sufficed to place the bit of paper with the shem in his mouth and he could become enraged to the point that everyone got out of his way. Only the rabbi knew how to stop him, and the people were well aware of this. The rabbi also knew that unfortunately humanity pays more attention to force than to good words. Then again, it sometimes utters such brash words that no power, no matter how great, can pull them back where they came from.

Emperor Rudolf, too, heard about the golem and wanted to possess him. The rabbi, however, took the golem to the emperor only for a visit, and demonstrated to the ruler what all the giant could do. Rudolf retracted his proposals for expelling the Jews, but expressed the wish that the rabbi create him a troop, a platoon, a whole regiment of such golems, who would tear down and destroy everything that stood in his way on the enemy's side.

And the rabbi now realized that not everything that is good for something is good for everything. He refused, and explained to the ruler that there can only be one golem, and when his service ended so would his life. Like a man, after death he would turn into dust. Thus commanded the Jewish Lord and it could not be otherwise. Not even the king had the right to change any of this.

Rudolf II responded with one of his typical frowns, but after a while the jester engaged him with his tricks. He broke into laughter, and the golem could return to the rabbi's house unharmed. The rabbi's wife was already waiting with a basket and piece of paper for the clay servant to buy her apples for strudel. The golem, too, seemed to be satisfied that he didn't have to light up another kind of fire in his head besides the light in his eyes. This clay giant didn't want to destroy or spoil anything. He didn't want to set foot where grass would not grow for two years after him. Anyway he was uneasy in the emperor's chambers. He was afraid to move, for fear of knocking down whatever shone, rang, clinked, and played around him, or even of stumbling into the lackey that whirled around the emperor more than the poodle one of the ladies of the court from the entourage of the beautiful favorite liked to fondle.

Instead of further satisfaction from the golem, the wise rabbi offered Rudolf something more innocent. At the court and below the Castle it was known that the emperor liked to listen to fairy tales – stories made up and real – and often had them told to him before he went to sleep. So the rabbi offered the emperor a fairy tale. The placated monarch could hear it the very next day.

It was about how the emperor's creditor, the rich Maisel, married the daughter of the first town councillor.

A Fairy Tale
for Rudolf II

Once upon a time a certain first town councillor was returning in his carriage from a late meeting of the council of lords. It was pitch black. In the cottages people were already sleeping. Before the councillor lay a forest path. The coachman strained his eyes to avoid leading the horses into the ditch. All at once, without anyone giving a sign to the horses, the coach stopped all by itself. The horses neighed, reared up, and refused to go on. Somewhere an owl could be heard. Dark. But a small light appeared in the darkness and came ever closer. There was a flickering in the brush along the road at the end of the town where the tardy one lived with his family. Suddenly the little light changed into a yellow-green glow and trembled like mist over a lake, like a will-o-the-wisp. As the glow increased, it dazzled the horses, the coachman, and the councillor.

The councillor, however, was not frightened by the strange spectacle. He got out of the coach resolutely and said: "I'm going to see what's going on there. The horses would be spooked."

He left the coachman behind with the horses and went. He couldn't believe his eyes. He was accustomed to feel out everything and investigate thoroughly, so he touched, and behold – there was the clink of gold. Yes, there was a pile of gold coins here that took one's breath way. What was it doing here? This and much else raced through the councillor's head. But try to think – what would occur to you? A person would not be lazy and would begin loading the pile into the coach with a shovel. Anybody would do the same – gather up quickly what had fallen from the sky or was rendered up by the earth for him. This for starters. Then he would race home so that the dream wouldn't dissolve before he woke up. And then he would deliberate over what to do with it. This would probably be the easiest part for us, of course.

However, the first councillor was still standing there and still hesitating. He looked around – and behold, he saw seven little dwarfs busily filling leather sacks with the coins and carrying them off one after the other into the dark. Finally the councillor got up the courage to speak:

"Where are you taking these sacks, and for whom?"

The dwarfs only laughed. It sounded like the clinking of the coins. The pile of gold disappeared behind the little men like a rainbow on the horizon. Only the glow still trembled and illuminated the scene of the action. If a blue flame with an orange tongue were not shining there in the grass, the councillor would think he had only dreamed all of this.

Suddenly the bearded dwarf ran up again, smothered the last little fire, did a somersault before the first councillor, and then gathered up lost coins from the grass.

"I thought you were going to leave them for me as a souvenir, so I would believe what I saw," the councillor dared to speak to the dwarf. "I really would like to know who they belong to and who they will belong to."

The dwarf finally stopped and said in a high voice:

"It's not good to know the future or ask about it, and I won't tell you anything."

The councillor stared at the little man with a pleading look. The little man began to fidget and scratched himself nervously behind the ear, but still said:

"If you won't have it any other way, I'll tell you. The money will belong to your daughter, but only after she gets married. Of course she'll be married in the Jewish Town," he added.

The councillor laughed at this. His daughter was still a little girl, and what could she have in common with some treasure? He didn't understand it. The dwarf noticed the skeptical smile and started to leave. Then he changed his mind and said:

"Alright, I'll give you the seven gold coins that were left, so that you'll always believe what you saw here. However, you must give me seven coins from your own sack because the total must agree."

Why not, the councillor thought, and counted out the money. Then the dwarf disappeared, the glow dissolved, and the little flame in the grass went out. The councillor boarded the coach; the calmed horses pounded their hooves into the earth and set into a trot. The councillor was home before a goat could lose a hair. But he couldn't fall asleep so quickly. He contemplated who it might be in the Jewish Town that would one day marry his daughter and bring her such a treasure, which actually belonged to him already today.

The next day he decided to play with fate and set out bait for this "rich man". He threw a gold coin into the street where he lived and which served as a large market place. Every day the place was teeming with people from early morning on. They came, went, ran here and there, and offered and bought the most varied goods. Many rich merchants ran about here until evening. The councillor looked out from the window of his apartment, watching how people passed by the gold coin as though it weren't there. And yet the sun above their heads shone on the coin and it sparkled brightly.

The councillor was still waiting behind the curtains of his room, and was about to draw them. The sun had now set. Along the street was skipping a freckled boy in tattered clothes, hands in his pockets, kicking a ball in front of him. Suddenly he caught sight of the coin, kneeled with lightning speed to the ground, and had it. He put it in his pocket, but oh! The coin slipped out through a hole in the pocket and rolled and rolled right under the councillor's windows. The boy left his ball in the middle of the street and chased after the coin. He crouched down for the second time and grasped the coin in his palm, but when he lifted

his eyes from the ground he dropped the coin again because in the window above him he saw a girl with black hair and a ribbon pale blue like the sky. She was watering the pink geraniums. The eyes of the two children met. The girl's pale face blushed and the boy leaned over for the coin for a third time. He grasped it firmly in his hand, smiled at the girl, and blew a kiss toward the window. And the councillor, who was standing behind the curtain in the window of the next room, frowned. This must be a mistake. "This dirty ragamuffin would make a strange husband for my daughter," he said to himself.

So he said to himself that he would repeat the experiment. Every day he thren out one coin – and every day it was picked up by the same boy. So the councillor decided to investigate more closely. He let the news be spread through the Jewish Town that he had lost several gold coins and would be glad if some honest person would report that he had found them. And behold! A boy with scraped knees and a torn pocket came to the councillor and handed over all the gold coins – except for one.

"Don't be angry, sir. I don't have that one any more, but as soon as I can I'll definitely bring it too."

"And what have you done with it?" the councillor wanted to know.

"I gave it to my mother, because she was lacking precisely one coin for a good opportunity she had to buy new merchandise."

The councillor smiled and said: "Look, my boy, you don't have to return anything. I'm surprised that you're so honest. Thank you. Not everybody would behave this way."

The boy shrugged his shoulders and declared: "My mother taught me that even if an apple rolls from the neighbors' tree onto our yard I must return it. That's what Moses taught, after all, and after him it was proclaimed by his brother Aaron. People should obey the commandments. If they did, then things would be fine in the world. I wish they were now."

The councillor heard out the scruffy boy, had new clothes and shoes brought to him for his honesty, and offered him a wash bowl with water. Immediately he became a fine-looking boy. When he examined the boy's appearance, which could be changed so easily, the councillor contemplated briefly. He knew well that human nature cannot be changed so easily. Either a person has it or he doesn't. So he believed that fortune was kind to him and his daughter in this respect. For a while he even forgot about the riches that had interested him, and was glad that his daughter would have a good and just man for a husband in the future.

Then he offered to help the boy's mother financially in the business, but this the boy adamantly refused: "Mother wouldn't accept it and father wouldn't either."

"Who is your father, anyway?" the councillor asked. Why, he knew perhaps every person in the Jewish Town.

"He's Shalum Maisel," answered the boy and, thanking the councillor, he hurried home. The councillor easily ascertained where the boy's family lived. One evening he took a walk and found Shalum Maisel at home alone. This suited him well – he wanted to have a talk with him undisturbed. He introduced himself and said:

"I'll take care of your son. I have the means to bring him up well."

"But he is already being brought up well," objected Maisel.

"Yes, I think so too, but I would like to give him an education. I'll take him with me on business trips so he can get to know the world and people. It's useful."

"I myself know best what is good for my son," protested Maisel. "He doesn't need an education to be a luggage-carrier, and a luggage-carrier he'll be, just as I was. It is good employment, honest and just. If he is honest and just, what better person could one want?"

The councillor once more and with greater effort tried to convince Maisel how nevertheless he could benefit the boy more.

"I don't want to part with my son. I don't want him to go out into the world. If nothing else, it would be a blow to his mother.

Why, he's our only surviving child; the others died in the plague. He's all that we have."

But the councillor didn't give up. He declared: "I understand you as a father, my good man. I too have only a single child, a daughter. But I'd like to give her as bride to your son and with her everything that I've saved. I like your son because of his honesty, which is not common today with young people."

Maisel conceded just a little: "You know what, councillor? Let it be and I will too. If it is to be the destiny of our children, as you think, I will not stand in his way, but he is still a child. Let's not look into the crystal ball today."

Time passed by, the cherries in Prague gardens ripened several times, and in the Jewish Town a young man and a girl grew up. They grew fond of each other and gave each other their word, and nobody prevented them in it. They decided to marry. The councillor couldn't wait for the day. He was curious about the money that the dwarf had predicted for him. After the wedding, however, several weeks passed and nothing special happened. So he decided to take the two young people to the site where the event had occurred long before. They came to the same place, but there was nothing there. Not even a trace of the gleaming long ago.

The councillor realized that he had probably been cheated, deceived by some kind of trickery. He became angry at himself, the dwarfs, his daughter, and her husband. He showed his displeasure to the young people in such an unpleasant way that one day they decided that the girl would leave her father, and they went to the parents of the young Maisel. His mother received the girl well and let them have a room behind the shop. She had a hardware business which was going quite well. Her husband kept the accounts and collected payments and everything was clicking along. They had as much as they needed for a decent living with some money saved for a rainy day.

One time the mother was buying something in a nearby town and went with the father for the merchandise. The young people

took her place in the store. A farmer came in and needed
a scythe for grain; it was just before harvest time. "Only," he
admitted, "just now I'm not able to pay; you would have to wait.
Or we'll do it another way."

"I'll wait," agreed the young Maisel. "You look like an honest
man. I believe you." He gave him as many scythes as he wanted,
but the farmer turned around at the door.

"Listen. You're a good and honest man. We'll do it another way
after all. At home I have an old iron chest that can't be opened.
Many musclemen have already tried, but nobody so far has been
able to do it. Take it as scrap iron – it will be a deposit on my
debt. Come for it."

Young Maisel took the address and went to that village for
the chest. He took it home on a cart, exerting himself like
crazy. He threw it into the courtyard – and hardly had it fallen
to the ground when it opened up by itself. The youth shook his
head at this, and when he lifted the cover what he saw almost
knocked him down. It was full of gold coins. He called his wife
and they decided to set out once again to see the farmer. They
loaded the money into sacks and struggled again with the cart
on their way back. They looked for the farmer's cottage with
the large courtyard and wide gate, but in vain. And yet it had
stood here; it was there before! They asked people, but they
shook their heads. "What? No such farmer is in the village here
and never was."

They decided to wait until the farmer showed up. They waited
a year, two years, and when the third year nobody showed up,
the young Maisel went to the rabbi and said:

"That's the way it happened. I have decided not to keep the
money for myself, even if I could enlarge mother's and my store
and buy a coach and a palace. What good would such
undeserved wealth be to me? A Jew likes to work, and earns
with his head and hands that which assures him a decent living.
I don't want anything for free, but I'm glad that I can give this
money to erect a new synagogue. And here you have it."

So they built a new synagogue and young Maisel could still give money to pave the streets, for construction of a Jewish hospital, and for a school. The new synagogue was opened ceremoniously. Flowers, toasts. All those present looked toward the corner where stood the one who made this possible. He was holding his wife's hand and, embarrassed, accepting tributes.

As he was thus looking around, he saw in another corner his father-in-law. Yes, the councillor was there, and his throat choked with emotion. Finally he overcame his stupid spite, came up, and embraced his daughter and son-in-law. At this moment all revenge, illwill, and hatred disappeared. The three embraced for a long time, and looked at each other lovingly. The councillor finally realized that to have such a man in the family is the greatest treasure. He wouldn't exchange him for a dwarf's pile of gold three times as high.

From that time on, when people spoke of the wisdom and careful judgement that characterized the young Maisel, it is said that they would tell a person who was to consider something properly: "Be a Maisel!"

Well, and after this outstanding member of the Jewish race is named one of the streets in Prague's Old Town.

The Beautiful Perla

A nother well-known Jewish tale pertains to the name of another Old Town street, called Perlová. Listen to it as Rudolf II listened.

Once by the River Warta in the old quarter of a Polish city a boy named Jehuda Liva ben Becalel was born to Rabbi Becalel. He grew up to be a clever young man, and so when he heard about the beautiful city in the Czech Kingdom, Prague, home at the time to one of the most famous Jewish schools in the world, he longed to go there. As soon as he reached the age of studies, he decided to set out for Prague. He parted with his parents and went.

At the time a rich Jew named Samuel Shmelke was living in the Jewish Town of Prague. He had a son and a daughter. The son settled in Poland in the town of Przemysl, where he did well and was honored and respected by all. The daughter Perla (meaning pearl) was a beautiful girl, truly like a pearl. Samuel sought a suitable bridegroom for her. He didn't want to give away such a beautiful and good daughter without deliberation. The young man Jehuda pleased him. He introduced the two children to each other and betrothed them. Jehuda was studying in Prague, but later he wanted to continue his studies in Poland. He bade farewell to Perla, her father, and her other family members, stroked the girl's hair, and swore that he would not abandon her.

He set out on his journey, and Samuel now remained alone with all the work. Woe to an old father if he has no son or

son-in-law at his side. His business floundered, his health failed, and Perla often wept in a corner of her room in the evening. She wept secretly so as not to add to her father's worries.

When Samuel was almost ruined, he finally sat down at his desk and wrote a letter to Jehuda in Poland: "I betrothed you with Perla because I thought I could give her a dowry. But misfortune, illness, and misery have come into my life, and those are evil sisters. Therefore I am relieving you of your promise to marry my daughter and take care of her. Marry where you want and whom you want, and don't feel bound to our family."

Jehuda answered the letter as follows: "Dear father of my beloved, if this is what Perla wants, I will obey. But I myself have no desire to marry another. I love Perla and love is not an equation with property on the other side."

And so Perla, a petite girl, decided that since there was not a man in the family just now, she would help her father in the business herself. Everybody liked to come into the store for goods when the girl was working, because she was not only beautiful but also pleasant and helpful. So they managed to make a bare living.

In the meantime Jehuda studied and made excellent progress. He thought about Perla and paid no attention to other rich and beautiful women that were offered to him.

Armies came again and with them further misery. One day a rider came into Prague's Jewish Town. A hungry soldier. The clothes on him were torn. His face was ashen like the horse under him, an old nag worn out with battle. The soldier jumped down from his horse, ran into the shop, took a loaf of bread from the counter, and started to run out quickly. Perla, however, blocked his way and said:

"Pay, soldier. We all must pay!"

"I don't have anything," the soldier objected. "I have nothing to pay with and I'm hungry."

"I support a family," said Perla, "and I'm hungry too."

"But for three days now I haven't eaten and I'll die if you don't let me have that bread, because I have no money. Wait, I have here a bolt of linen. You're a woman, maybe you would have use for it. I'll leave the linen as security. If I don't return by evening, keep the linen and use it as you want. My mother gave it to me when I went to war so I'd have something for a shirt when I come back. They killed my mother, and what use will a shirt be to me, one, two, or ten, if I die of hunger. It would be a waste to use it for my burial garb."

The youth jumped on his horse and rode away.

It took a while for Perla to recover and tell the story to her father. He nodded his gray head and said: "We're not the only ones for whom war and misery have made life difficult. What can we do? We'll do without bread: boil potatoes. But don't touch that bolt of linen. It was a gift from a mother to a poor son when he had to go into bloody battle."

Perla placed the bolt high on a shelf and continued to work, to help her father. Meanwhile she thought about Jehuda – how he was faring and what would happen in the future.

Jehuda wrote by candlelight to his beloved that he would never abandon her for money and that he would keep the promise to her father that he would take care of her honorably.

"The misery I've come to grieves me all the more," wailed old Samuel. "He is an honest man and you could live well together."

"But we will, father." Perla stroked her father's gray hair. "You'll see that one day we will."

A year passed. Nobody came for the roll of linen. The next year Jehuda was to finish his studies in Poland.

Two years passed from the time when the poor man in a soldier's uniform on the old nag untied the bolt of linen from the side of the horse and exchanged it for a loaf of bread so as not to die. Even the old Samuel now judged that the soldier would not return. So Perla blew the dust off the bolt and decided to sew what she could from the linen and sell it in the store. She unwound the bolt. Something clinked on the floor. She wanted to reach down under the table. The bolt continued to open. And as Perla unwound the linen further and further, ducats veritably jumped out of the fabric until there was a fine pile of them.

They couldn't even cry out in joy: the words stuck in the throats of both father and daughter. They embraced each other and old Samuel sat down and wrote immediately to Jehuda in Poland: "So we're waiting for you, son! A miracle has happened. Perla will have a dowry; you can get married. How did this come about? It must have been the prophet Elijah himself, but I'll tell you all in detail when you return."

Jehuda came. He still insisted that his greatest wealth was Perla, who was a true pearl. He would use the money wisely for a God-fearing life as a couple and later for three.

And so Jehuda married Perla and became a Prague rabbi. He was immensely wise, learned, and strong, and they called him Löw (lion) because he was a lion among scholars. Anyway Bruncvík had a lion under the Stone Bridge and the Czech lands had a special fondness for lions.

The Golem
as a Baker

he golem served the rabbi's wife for a long time. He went again and again to the fish merchant and the baker, brought home in a basket whatever he had written on his note, and knew how to bow in greeting and to express thanks. With the little fire in his eyes he showed lesser or greater pleasure or indifference. He had such strength that he could carry a great quantity and a heavy burden, and thus he helped conserve human strength and human steps.

The golem Josef, servant of Rabbi Löw and his wife, guarded the ghetto, helped in the kitchen, was a friend to their daughter Ester, and stood as the guardian of peace between Christians and Jews in Prague. Relations between Christians and Jews, however, gradually changed. After the golem brought the servant girl to court as a living witness and thus helped refute the monstrous story of her death and the shedding of blood, Czech people no longer believed the slanders about the drinking of Christian blood at Jewish ceremonies.

With the golem it was the same as with every similar being in which there is too much energy, fire, and water but no reason or feeling. He was as they created him, and resembled a human without feeling and without wisdom, who was not educated to think first and then act. He blindly obeyed orders, and later imitated what he saw others doing. As long as he worked and was beneficial with his strength, his activity was useful. But as soon as he acted without contemplation and without thinking, misfortune and ruin set in. If he had enough tasks assigned to him, he had no time to seek others.

It sometimes happened that people rather forgot about him, and so he wandered the streets like a weighty barrel full of fire, and all fled before him. Beneath his feat the earth shook and where there was snow or ice they melted beneath his eyes in floods in the street. Thus the golem walked through the Jewish town and looked into windows, and little children got seizures from it.

One morning the clay Josef set out again into the streets when the town was still sleeping. Only one window was shining, and the golem stopped by it. He watched how a girl was waking up. She'd rather continue sleeping. Her eyes were half closed to the world, half opened to the new day. She stretched, then put on her skirt, blouse, and apron. In a vessel of water she washed her eyes and face, and scrubbed her hands up to the elbows. She took a brush and combed out her hair down to her waist, braided it, and fastened it with pins. The golem followed all this without interest. Such things didn't fascinate him.

However, as soon as the girl went to the large oven behind the door of her room and tried to light it, striving in vain to start a fire with the starter, the golem tapped on the window. At first the girl was afraid, but then she recognized Josef. She knew that he often came to the neighbor to buy things and brought the rabbi's wife everything she needed, and that he had strength and fire. She was also afraid of his anger if she didn't open the door. He could break her window and awake all the others. And the girl had the task of baking bread and rolls for the residents of two streets.

So she opened the door. The golem went to the oven, leaned over, and the fire radiating from his eyes kindled the wood. A log burst into flame and the girl rejoiced. She stroked the golem and quickly went into the pantry for flour. She wanted to pour it from a large sack into an enormous kettle. The golem pushed her aside, grabbed the sack of flour as though it were a match stick, and poured into the kettle as much as the young baker needed. "That's enough, Josef!" she ordered, and began mixing. But he didn't allow her that, either, and so she let her helper do all her work in her place. She then only formed loaves and rolls and arranged them on large tins, and the golem placed them into the oven. He waited for the girl to nod and pulled them out again.

Work went well for the young baker this way! The whole week she always waited in the morning, and when she saw her helper in the dim light outside the window, she let him in and then sat herself in front of a mirror to make herself pretty. She had more time for herself and lost interest in work. Why, she had somebody to do it for her! The rolls were crisp and there were three times as many of them as she could ever manage to make herself. If she had Josef mix larger batches in the kettle, she sold the bread before the other bakers could be ready. She carried her head very high when they began praising her art, ability, work, and beauty.

Many young men stopped at her door who would have liked to have her as a wife because of her positive attributes. One of them pleased the girl, and therefore one day she invited him to supper. The youth brought wine. They talked, made merry, and completely forgot that morning was approaching.
Then somebody knocked on the window.

"Go, quickly run away!" cried the girl to the youth. But he didn't feel like it.

"Why? Who's coming to see you so early? Why, go and open the door!" said the groom.

"It's only my helper," said the baker girl, and heard renewed pounding on the window. She wanted to open the door before Josef broke the window, but after all she couldn't betray her secret to her lover. She liked him so much!

"Helper? You didn't say you had a helper," said the young man, surprised. "So why don't you let your helper in? At least I'll get to meet him."

What could the girl do? She went into the entry hall and opened the door. The golem lumbered into the bakery.

"Lord!" called out the man in horror. But Josef went directly to the oven, started the fire, went into the pantry, grabbed the sack, and did what he did every day.

Only now did the youth realize how he had been deceived by the girl. She wasn't so industrious as she let it be heard around town. On the contrary! Thanks to her better and timely merchandise, well-mixed by the effort of another and soon renowned throughout the Old Town, every baker in the vicinity lost business and earnings.

The youth went out the same door he had come in by, and never showed up again. The girl wept for three days and three nights. And what's more, she couldn't get rid of the golem. He continued to come to her and baked larger and larger quantities of bread until all the flour was used up. In a rage he then trampled the bakery to pieces, so that the girl had to go weeping to the rabbi. She told him all, confessed everything, and the rabbi's wife took the part of the poor girl. Why, it was their Josef who caused this, after all. They took a collection for the girl and built her a new bakery. In time a new bridegroom turned up and he took up the work that the golem had done. He carried sacks of flour, started the fire in the large oven, and placed the heavy tins. The beautiful baker girl could once more sleep longer and take longer in combing out her black hair down to the waist, but she alone formed the loaves and rolls with hands white from flour. They said that no one could knead them as well as she could.

The Golem
as a Servant

fter the incident with the young baker girl the golem more than once performed work that was useful but less than necessary. When the rabbi's wife ran out of wood, Josef didn't wait for her to order more. He set out into the forest on the edge of Prague and saw lumberjacks there. They were felling trees that had been damaged by weather. As soon as they saw the golem, they took fright and fled into a ravine to hide. With relish, the golem began ripping trees out of the earth like beets. He cut the branches off the trunks using the axe they had left, hoisted the logs on his shoulders, and carried them off to the rabbi's house. It was beautiful and healthy wood and so they were all horrified as to where Josef had gotten it.

When the fishermen had their harvest time, the rabbi's wife sent the golem to buy fish. For a while he stood and observed what the fishermen were doing, then he set out for all the ponds in the vicinity of Prague and emptied them. He carried off baskets full of fish that were left floundering in the mud. If it weren't for the good Old Town merchants all the fish would have died. But the golem brought in water and carried the fish off to those who bought them. That year the fishermen had no work, but business in the Jewish Town flourished.

People in the Jewish Town and elsewhere in Prague became more and more afraid of the golem's strength and boredom and lack of wisdom. "What all he has done already!" they said to themselves. He tore down dams and houses, ripped out trees by the roots, and swept away everything that blocked his way. He

was capable of fiery anger and the chill of water. But he didn't have much of the sun, which makes nature fruitful at the right time and inactive at the right time. The sun, which strengthens, smooths, and illuminates beauty and longing in the human soul. The golem had in himself fire without inhibition, dangerous at any time and exploitable at any time.

People feared the golem everywhere where they had something to fear for. In the Old Town lived old Aaron, a cloth merchant. He was a good businessman, the pride of the guild and joy of his family. He lived and worked for his family. He thought about its future and worked into the last years of his life. He had a wife, two sons, and a daughter, and employed all of them in the store.

Many times already it seemed as he aged that he would depart from life, but hardly had he lain down when he rose again and was fine. It was only his spine, bent for years over the fabric he offered to ladies. It hurt and needed to rest occasionally.

The time came, however, when old Aaron lay down never to rise again. He wrote a will, gave everyone his blessing, bade his farewells, and wished his wife and children good business and a good living for their remaining days without him. He instructed everyone individually how to act and how much to charge this and that customer, how he or she should be sparing with the fabric and measure it out so as not to part with even a millimeter extra. He even betrayed where he had money stashed away for years for repair of the shop, where he was keeping it for the worst times. He confided to his wife where the most expensive bolt of cloth lay, from which she once had wanted to sew clothes, but he had wanted to save it and sell it when the price of the fabric rose.

The wife stroked Aaron's cheek and his thinning hair and told him to stop uttering such nonsense. Why, that which was most precious in the world to her was leaving her. Aaron was moved by his wife's devotion and urged his sons to share with each other honestly and to take good care of their mother, his widow. He instructed his daughter not to marry that ragged man next door who couldn't keep his eyes off her, and said that with the help of her brothers she should seek a rich merchant, of which there were quite a few in the Jewish Town, and join her life and her dowry with him.

The wife wiped a tear from her eye, and the children held their father's hands. They gave him a cup of tea. He sipped, set the cup on the tray, and suddenly whispered:

"Isaac, my son, do you have all the merchandise in stock?"

"Yes, father, don't worry, just sleep peacefully. Close your eyes and don't worry about anything."

The father dozed off for a little while and his family sat by him, deeply moved. They were all present. Both sons and the spouse faithful to him in work and in love. The servant girl and the daughter were there too. By the bed was a candle, and its flame occasionally trembled from the breath of whoever spoke. They whispered so that the father could find relief in sleep. After a while the ailing man said in a half sleep:

"Are you here, my Ester?"

The woman gave a start – in that quiet and sadness she had almost fallen asleep, too.

"Yes, I'm here, my dear husband," she said, and took her husband's hand into her own.

"And what about Leo, is Leo here too?" Aaron asked.

From the back a quiet voice was heard. "Of course I'm here with you, daddy."

"That's good," whispered the old man. After a while he turned on his side. With half-closed eyes he sighed wearily and asked again:

"Isaac is still here, too?"

"How could I leave? Of course I'm here with you!"

It seemed that the father calmed down, but then he asked about the last of his children: "And what about Miriam, my beloved daughter, where is she?"

She stroked her father's cheek and said: "Daddy, how could I not be with you? Every moment with you is dear to me. I'm your daughter, aren't I?"

For a while silence set in. Such a silence as blankets everything and fosters resignation and a feeling that everything is as it should be, according to the Lord's will.

But the man suddenly opened his eyes and cried out: "What am I hearing, what are you saying? So if you're all here around me, then who's watching the shop?"

Their blood froze in their veins, they were so surprised by their father's sudden question, which seemed needless to them. But in order to calm his already weakened mind, all present winked at each other, and the maid in the back answered:

"Don't worry. I called the rabbi's golem. He's in the store. He's unwinding the bolts and guarding the shop."

At this the man jumped out of bed and stormed: "So the golem, you say the golem?" And just as he was, in a white night shirt sewn from his store's best linen, he ran out of the room and down the stairs. The shop was closed, the blinds down. A funeral wreath was by the gate.

There is no need to tell you how the five hearts in the apartment over the shop trembled and pounded. The sons ran down after their father and helped him back to bed. But the man stayed in it only until morning, and the next day he was standing behind the counter. He couldn't trust even his own family. And then – what if that golem happened to walk by?

Old Aaron lived another ten years with his family after this event. Before his candle finally burned out, he lived to see grandchildren and unwound many more meters of fabric. He spoke many words about it and convinced half of Prague that his goods were the best in the world.

The Golem
Saves the Ghetto

mong the greatest horrors besides the bloody
pogroms were fires and the floods experienced
especially by the already-mentioned tanners and
leather-dyers. They lived on the banks of the Vltava
because they needed water more than the famous
necessity salt, but the water rose so high in some floods that
many families had to quickly move out of their inundated houses.
Some buildings couldn't withstand such onslaughts of water
and had to be torn down.

As long as the golem was with Rabbi Löw everything was fine.
The afflicted came to him and the strong creature served them.
He erected anew what the water had destroyed, if there
hadn't been too much of it and if it hadn't disturbed the structure
to its foundations. He easily lifted large stones like children's
building blocks and placed them where they were supposed to be.

When after one terrible cloudburst the whole Jewish Town was
flooded, the rabbi gave the golem the shem and a slip of paper
with the instruction to build a stone dam! Because the rains last-
ed seven days and seven nights, the dam prevented much water
from continuing to spill over the banks of the Vltava. The people
shouted praises to the golem, but human feelings and fads did
not affect his stone life. He did what he had been ordered to do.

And when some evil people with ill intent tried to utilize the
golem's abilities to start a fire, they couldn't succeed – without the
shem it wasn't possible. The golem also had in his memory a permanent order to obey only his masters at home, and he recog-

nized them well even in the dark. Then, too, only the rabbi and his family had the shem. It was a different matter when one of them forgot about Josef. Then things happened! Fortunately the golem rather helped to put out a fire when it struck the Jewish Town. He carried more water than twenty men could have done.

The golem was simply a strong man par excellence. He still had plenty of strength left even when it was necessary to replace the shem. He did a fine piece of work. When in a cruel winter the ice cutters couldn't persuade the Vltava to give up its ice, which they were to distribute, they were on the verge of despair. Fortunately they remembered Josef. Hardly had they drawn long rectangles for him on the frozen river when the golem leaned on them with his feet and the ice blocks broke free. The ice cutters merely passed the pieces from one to another onto carts drawn by horses.

Once, thieves in the Old Town were planning to climb over the wall of the ghetto and carry off the golden treasure the Jews had long been hoarding for bad times. There were twelve of them, but they didn't know that the golem was standing ready for them on the other side. As the first four slithered down above the gate, the golem seized one after the other and thren them back over the wall. They were so bruised that they never again dared to come near these parts.

When poor Matis needed to build a little house and had no money to buy materials, the golem cut him enough stone from a cliff. Another time, on the other hand, he helped by tearing down houses and structures beyond the walls of Prague when enemies were marching on it. He thus completely, barred their military camp, so that Prague shone on them nicely. For Prague soldiers who had to go quickly to battle, he baked bread and also carried a basket of it to pious women who were praying for their soldier sons. He burned the enemy's supplies, carried off their ammunition and arms, chased the horses from their stables, and broke up their military formations. The shots they fired at him didn't do any good. They bounced off his massive body like bread crumbs. So they fled from him in horror as fast as they could.

Thus the golem Josef saved Prague including the Jewish quarter. It also happened that an improper girl was walking home late at night and encountered the golem. She was so thoroughly horrified that she never went out of the house after dark again. Other girls also learned from her example, so they no longer engaged in any mischief in abandoned streets as they do and did in other times.

It also happened that the golem proved how, thanks to his strength not bound to human reason and memory, he himself could not only serve but also harm.

Every Friday evening before the great Saturday prayer sessions, the golem received a new shem and had to obey the orders. One day, however, the rabbi's little daughter Ester fell ill. The father stood over her in deep pain for such a long time that for the first time in his life he forgot about everything else, including the fact that it was Friday evening.

So he called a man and conveyed that the congregation should start praying the Saturday worship, and that he himself would elevate himself with them through silent prayer at the bed of his daughter. It was the tenth verse of the Kabala shabat when a man came into the room and shouted: "The golem! Horror, the golem!"

Indeed. The golem was running through the school like an evil demon, throwing everything around until the building shook. Candelabras were rolling on the floor. The rabbi's wife had her kitchen full of water, fish, and wood. Nobody had told Josef "enough"! Nobody had taken the shem from him. Even the worship service in the synagogue was spoiled, and the prayer "Mizmer shir liom Hashabat" was interrupted and had to be repeated. From that time on, the Old-New Synagogue has been the only synagogue where, in memory of this event, this prayer is said twice.

At this moment the rabbi told the people to stop praying. He took the shem from the golem and thus his power waned. The rabbi bowed to the Almighty, and Malach Hamavod, the angel of death, withdrew from little Ester's bed. The girl opened her eyes, stretched out her hands to her father, and called for her mother. She had recovered.

Where did the Golem Josef Go?

 Days and months unwound from the ball of yarn of the time in which the golem Josef was among people. He did much that was beneficial but also did harm, and as usual, people forgot about the good and began to fear the golem and point to the bad.

Several times the rabbi bewailed the damage that the golem occasionally caused. He blamed himself. Therefore he convened the whole council of the congregation and pondered: "Is the golem still needed to guard the Jewish congregation? To arouse fear in people? No! Jews and Christians have now learned to coexist. They have come to know each other and understand that they can live peacefully alongside each other. The law punishes all to the same degree and protects the wronged on both sides."

The rabbi decided to summon those who stood at the birth of the golem Josef and would thus be present at his end. He ordered his ward: "Golem Josef, today you shall sleep in the attic of the Old-New Synagogue!"

He sent a servant for his son-in-law, who came and brought with him the rabbi's pupil. They sat down opposite the rabbi and listened to his proclamation: "Because you were present at the golem's creation, I want you to be here at his end. Today we must call from life that which we brought into it."

The golem obeyed his master and lay down to sleep in the attic of the Old-New Synagogue. Hardly had dusk fallen when three figures emerged from the rabbi's house. They were Rabbi Löw, his son-in-law, and his pupil. It was a dark night, without stars, just as it was when they created the golem. His life was to expire in darkness, just as his birth was in darkness.

Meanwhile Josef lay down in the attic of the synagogue and fell asleep. As he lay down, the floor under him shuddered, as though the bell of death were tolling the end. He fell asleep immediately and did not hear the voices around him, nor the quiet steps of the men, nor how they placed a lantern by his head. Then the rabbi spoke again:

"As a man returns to the earth, from which he drew all nourishment throughout his life, the golem too will return to the clay from which he arose as a child from its mother."

Then the three men positioned themselves so as to form a triangle. They stood as the angels of death by the head of the golem. Slowly and seriously, quietly and with dignity, they sang the words of the well-known song about the creation of man. Meanwhile they looked with sympathy at the sleeping giant. They watched how his firm, hard breast slowly rose to these words, slowly and still more slowly, as when the life strength is ebbing from a human.

"Now, now is the time," whispered the rabbi. He bowed to the two men and to the golem, that strange friend of clay, a helper in hard work and in difficulties with people. To the one whom kings and emperors wanted to destroy their neighbors, to burn forests and fields and the homes of their opponents whose land they wanted. What all the golem might do in the hands of the irresponsible! And who would have it all on his conscience? How would he answer to the Lord for this one day? So the rabbi pondered silently, and silently bowed his head over the golem, who in his strength was innocent and for whose evil deeds in the future too only an evil man could be responsible.

The rabbi reached into the golem's open mouth and took the shem out. Both of the two other men held their breath. It was a short moment of sacred excitement and horror over this wonder of nature, of human hand, and of the human mind, which in combination could achieve great things. They pondered what it would mean to give this enormous destructive matter the opportunity to act on its own, or to control it in good faith, or what a human with ill intent could destroy with it. No, there was no other choice than that which they had decided on – to take him quickly away from people and the world. Not every man would be capable of a deed that required such deliberation. Only a true human with all the marks of humanity and a human with a great heart could do so.

The golem was no longer breathing. The rabbi said to his son-in-law: "Come, husband of my beloved daughter, and stand here. And you, my most obedient and brightest pupil. Repeat after me precisely that which I will do."

Then the rabbi once more bowed to the golem and walked around him seven times backwards. The young men did precisely the same after him. The rabbi's son-in-law, who called out of the golem's body the powerful element of fire, and the rabbi's pupil, who disconnected from him the important element of water. What is matter without water? That is soon understood even by a small child. And all people can explain without hesitation what life is without fire.

The golem became once more mere matter, clay. The men took from Josef the clothes he had worn during his life resemble a man. They covered the body with old vestures from the attic. They surrounded him with Hebrew books bound in leather. The golem lay peacefully as lie kings and great men of nations, thinkers, and artists, all who came as guests to this world, to this planet, through the will of the Almighty. But then came the final day.

In the Jewish Town, later called Josefov, the people found out immediately the next day that the golem Josef had travelled away somewhere and would never return. At first they were surprised – what, so suddenly? But when they indeed neither saw or heard anything of him, nor even a sign, they believed it. And some were glad.

The rabbi himself confirmed the news of the golem's final journey – and he was not lying. Just one little thing nagged peoples' minds from that day on: why was nobody allowed to open the attic of the Old-New Synagogue, and why was there a heavy lock hanging on the door from that day on? Most took this as a commandment. Why, what business is it of ours? The rabbi has his precious books and valuables there. He has the right to give orders.

But only he himself and the two young men at his side knew what the real reason was: fear of some malicious hands, humanly mischievous, who would try to bring the golem to life once more for evil purposes, for their own benefit and to the detriment of humanity.

The Golem as Hope

he golem was not forgotten. All over Prague, stories of his deeds were told and became legends. After some time the Jewish people asked once more if it would not be possible to bring the golem back. Secretly they invoked his power, but in vain. They had to rely only on themselves, on the fate destined for them and read in the stars by Rudolf's astronomer. In vain they implored the Lord to resurrect the one who by fire and the glow of his body would destroy the enemies who wreaked violence on them. And that violence came many more times. No miracle occurred. Only the yellow Jewish stars still shone over the hooks of the crosses on which man hung man. Whole rows of lanterns then glowed with the flames of human suffering.

And yet humanity should have progressed long ago to the point where the golem was not necessary. So thought even his creator, Rabbi Löw, already at the time when the Prague people, always tolerant and capable of understanding human matters, took a long time before they accepted the Jews as partners. Only later and slowly, and with wise caution, did Jews and Christians in Prague join together and share their suffering, which culminated during the last world war.

The prophecy of the astronomer Tycho de Brahe, who is sleeping his eternal sleep in the Týn Church as he wished, had come true. From his tomb it is not too far to Rabbi Löw's final resting place – from the Old Town Square to the Old Jewish

Cemetery it is but a short walk. The astronomer, who predicted that the Jewish people would one day have their own country if they refrained from taking the land of others by force, believed that their star would shine in peace very high in the sky. However, the gas in which their hopes dissolved did not reach above the clouds, and so the stars could not hear the human wailing and suffering.

Other astronomers sought an answer in the stars for years in vain. Why? The time had long past when the wise Cohen came with clasped hands to the Pope to relieve Emperor Ferdinand of Habsburg of the oath that he would expel not only non-Catholics, but above all Jews from his empire. The slanders that the Jews caused the epidemic of the plague in Prague and that they conspired with the Germans against Maria Theresa had long ago evaporated.

The first and second world wars came and went. Tourists from all over the world visit the sites of the tragedies of this century. What will the next century bring?

The golem remains a legend. Children draw his clumsy figure and ask, "Where is he? Will he come? Could I tame the golem?" Hey! Tame? Yes, it happened once already and the tamed golem ran around the Old Town until he met his end.

"Where is the golem? You say they laid him to rest in the synagogue? May we see him?" Thus query adults.

"You cannot," says Rabbi Karol Sidon, and the teacher Mr. Feuerlich adds: "What could remain of him after four centuries? What remains of a human? Of matter? The clay has disintegrated in the old attic, and pigeons have carried away the dust. Only the legend has remained."

Others are being born.

The Golem is Only Sleeping

I t is said that during the second world war the Jewish synagogue, museum, and cemetery were visited by German soldiers who came to Prague unwelcome. Such a small group of young men in uniforms, curious about everything they had not seen yet, was walking through the cemetery. The German names on the gravestones perhaps restrained their more caustic remarks. At some things they wondered, at others they laughed. Why, the holocaust had come, the final pogrom on the Jews, about whom they had known so far so little – only that in place of the sign of the cross they had the sign of a six-pointed star. They were different from Christians. Some had the typical facial features of the Jewish race, while on others you couldn't tell at all that Jewish blood was coursing in their veins.

These youths could imagine and think anything, because a young person has his own ideas and relies on pure suppositions if he wants to remake the world. These young soldiers, however, were already that which Hitler wanted – in their heads they no longer had anything but Hitler's ideology, whose goal above all was to exterminate, to liquidate the Jews. And because most rich Jews managed to escape from Europe before the Nazi terror, the Hitlerites vented their frustration all the more on the ordinary Jews who carried their bundles and walking sticks along the hard paths of their ancestors and previous generations. However, many Jews also joined the ranks of the armies that formed on the fronts of the second world war, and fought against the occupiers.

But woe to those who remained and to those whom others betrayed and whose hiding places they revealed. With a bloody net all over Europe that caught every Jew, Hitler arrogantly carried his head high, and his deeds could be compared in their monstrousness only with the witch hunts or Nero's torches. There is no difference in cruelty between Christians and pagans when fanaticism reaches the pinnacle of evil. Every form of fanaticism is insane and dangerous to the world.

The group of soldiers was too young to know much about the world. However, pride was cultivated in them, and a feeling of national superiority. They let it be known everywhere they went, to people on the streets who preferred to get out of their way, and to waiters in restaurants. They turned up their noses and spoke loudly to let it be known who the master was here, that this land belonged to them from this time on, that they also owned the people, from which they would pick out their chosen ones and send the others the way of the Jews, because Hitler had grand plans for the world.

The youths sat down in a nearby pub and asked the waiter what he could offer them. He brought them a menu and the young men finally took off their caps, hung them on the rack, and set about eating. They drank the food down with good beer and rejoiced that things in Prague really were good, especially for men in uniform, and that they would have a good look around here. They began to take an interest in Jewish homes and the synagogue. They called to the waitress, and because nobody else was present in the pub at the moment, they asked her to sit down with them. She felt awkward. To sit with German soldiers would be like taking pleasure in their visit, like agreeing with the policy of occupation. The head waiter, however, nodded his head to her that she should keep them company for a while. He knew that as soon as more guests turned up in the pub they would relieve her of the unpleasant task.

But the voice, eyes, and proud forehead of one blue-eyed soldier pleased the waitress. He also had the highest rank. He ordered the head waiter to bring another glass, poured the girl a drink, and then asked her to tell him about that Jewish street and the Jewish houses, and how it was possible that there was a whole Jewish town here, and what this or that landmark or name meant.

Laughing, the girl proclaimed, "I'm no guide. I know the prices of food, how to serve guests, and the quality of liqueurs and beer, but I don't know individual houses. I only know that the statue on our Paris Street represents Moses."

"Moses?" the young men exclaimed. "But Moses gave the Christians the ten commandments. What do the Jews have to do with that?"

"I don't know," the girl shrugged her shoulders, "but I heard that Moses's brother was Aaron."

A soldier who was listening to the conversation of these two said after a while, "Let's leave the landmarks alone and raise our glasses. Not long from now the Jews will have a different monument, when there is no trace of them left."
The others raised their glasses with a laugh, stood, and toasted: "To Moses!"

They laughed wantonly and poured another glass:
"To Aaron!"

Soon the merry Germans were yelling throughout the pub.

"Let's have a third!" called the German officer and beckoned to the girl to raise her glass as well, because now it would be: "To the beautiful Czech waitress!"

When they had emptied the bottle and had another brought, the head waiter didn't like it anymore and called the girl away, saying the miss must serve the guests who had just arrived. The soldiers were sorry and promised to get together more often with the beautiful Prague girl.

The girl offered them her hand and then remembered: "Why, I actually do know something interesting about the Jewish Town and the Old-New Synagogue, as they call it here."

The soldiers listened with curiosity as the girl told them the story of the golem.

"What? So he was buried here? Among those old gravestones we'll find his final resting place?"

"Not at all," she laughed. "Do you think they would lay a stone giant into a grave? They say they laid his body in the attic of the synagogue, where he would sleep until somebody brought him back to life. Maybe he's still sleeping there today, upstairs in the attic of the synagogue."

"Who has the keys to that attic?" they asked.

"The legend says that Rabbi Löw had them. He is lying in the cemetery. He threw the key away so that nobody would think of disturbing the golem's peace."

The soldiers guffawed: "The golem's peace! Hah! Old wives' tales! Somebody must have that key!"

In vain the frightened girl tried to explain to them that this was not the case. But let them try what nobody had ever tried – to find that key. In the town hall lived the teacher who had told her that story a long time before. He was old, knew a lot, and tried to accommodate everyone to the best of his ability.

The soldiers, exhilarated by wine and gabbing with the beautiful girl, took her advice and set out after the teacher who lived next to the Old-New Synagogue. They asked him to let them in and take them through the building. He was glad to oblige. However, it immediately seemed to him that these soldiers had quite a different intent, because his narrative didn't interest them at all. So he truncated his explanations and the officer whom the waitress had liked so much blurted out directly: "You haven't told us the main thing yet. We want to see your merriest character – the golem."

The teacher saw that the soldiers were intoxicated, but nevertheless he tried to explain to them calmly: "The golem? He has entered into legend."

The soldiers laughed: "Christ entered into heaven, so the golem entered into legend." There was no end to their gall.

The teacher preserved his calm and dignity, only pointing out: "But it was such a long time ago."

"Yes," said one of the soldiers, "so why don't you show us where he was laid to rest? In the attic, right? Who has the key to that attic?"

The old man saw that further explanations would be entirely pointless and undignified in this building, and tried to lead the soldiers out, but he couldn't do so. The officer got angry and bellowed on behalf of all of them:

"How dare this man? But he'll soon go where he probably belongs. Bind him with a belt, sit him on a chair and we'll go have a look ourselves. What do we need a key for? I'll shoot open the door to the attic. First I'll try to force the lock with a knife. How dare this man here try to forbid something to members of our nation, its representatives? You don't give orders here any more. We give orders to you!"

That was the attitude the soldiers took toward the old taboo, which until that time nobody had violated. They felt like having a look at what was really hidden in the attic. They bound the teacher and agreed that the officer with the blue eyes would go first, try to pave the way, then call to the others.

So the officer started up the steps and was already anticipating how he would present himself to that dear girl as the hero of the day, the year, that whole period of the 1940s.

When he left, the soldiers lit up cigarettes. As a joke they put one in the mouth of the poor teacher, who was praying silently, mortified by his disgrace and the disgrace of a building sacred to thousands of people.

They smoked three cigarettes, gabbed, and even sang, and paid no attention to the teacher. But all at once one of them remembered:

"What is Fritz doing up there so long? Maybe he found some treasure there and doesn't want to share it with us?"

"Let's go after him!" suggested another.

"Who'll guard the teacher?" the others hesitated.

"OK, I'll go have a look myself and call you," he said and ran toward the stairs leading to the attic. In a moment he was back.

"My God, friends, come and help me! Fritz is lying by the attic. The knife is thrust in the door and the door is locked."

All ran up to the attic and brought down their officer. The beautiful blue eyes were open, and horror stared out of them. He was dead.

They untied the teacher, didn't say a word, and called to their command. A hearse came for their leader.

Thanks to the fact that they had unbound the teacher, he could clasp his hands in prayer. He prayed for the poor officer and for those like him in their pride and conduct. He prayed for all individuals and whole nations that the time of war and the time of the rule of Nero would pass, and that the Lord of the Jews and the God of Christians would give the world wise and good citizens as long as living creatures inhabited the earth.

But nobody ever found out what actually happened by the attic door which that curious, proud young man tried to open.

As the seasons alternate, the towers of Prague are veiled by the mists of colorful autumns, the gold of summer illuminates the clouds in the sky, and white blankets of snow chastely cover the nakedness of endless winters with long waiting for the merciful spring. Beneath the towers, merciful time carries away the events experienced. New events arrive and materialize on the stage of humanity, and everything is repeated: loves and hates, periods of creation and of destruction, peaceful years and times of war, efforts of those who cultivate the land, and ruin and violence. Baseness and vain desires to own as much as possible of this planet as soon as possible, now, immediately, before death drops the curtain on human life.

The towers of Prague churches raise their fingers to the overcast sky and plead for mercy in hard times, like the prayers of those who stand beneath the thirteenth – century gothic arches of the Old-New Synagogue. The towers glitter with copper gilding among green trees under the blue sky. In just this way for centuries all those to whom Prague has been home, a cradle full of the most beautiful dreams, have bravely lived in this city alongside each other.

Let us stop especially in Prague's Jewish Town. With its architectural treasures, it has remained to this day a history of those who once came to Bohemia, and chose and were granted this part of Prague for their homes. It has survived fires, heavy losses in the attacks of the crusaders and fanaticized mobs, and humiliation by others who wished it ill. It has survived centuries of wrongs and insults, but also the joy of fulfilled hopes in the justice and friendship of other Praguers.

Under the arches of these churches and synagogues, they believed that their Almighty looks after all in common, whatever name they might give him. That he looks after those who contributed blood and sweat and suffered the pain of humiliation for the faith and for good. Above the stars, he watches and waits, just as a just person waits on this earth, for neighbors to clasp each others' hands in understanding, because only from all these hands clasped in a single long chain can no destructive element arise that could punish the world with a horrible pogrom.

Many tourists from all lands on all continents have come to Prague to see its beauty. On the Jewish holidays, when Rosh Hashana – the Jewish New Year – is observed seriously by meditating in the synagogue from Saturday morning until Sunday, pious Jews do not sit in pubs and do not drink alcohol. They dip their bread in honey and symbolically eat carp heads, because Rosh Hashana is the head of the year. In the early spring, when the banks of the Vltava begin to loose their last snow – the days of the Jewish "purium" – after prayers they come to the river and there "turn open their pockets" to pour out all their sins, major and minor, into its waves. Let the flowing waters carry them to the unknown. After the holidays comes fasting in memory of Gedaili, the governor of Jerusalem, who was murdered by enemies after the destruction of the Temple, as explained by today's chief rabbi of the Czech Republic, Efraim Karol Sidon.

Along with tourists, they then stop over the graves of their ancient ancestors and relatives, who have various graves as in other cemeteries. On days when Prague glows with sunny reflections, when gilded foliage plays with steps and has the colors of an artist's pallet, and in times of white peace, the humble and grateful descendants come to stop by the gravestones with names long unspoken among the living. Only a few of them have survived the passage of time.

We find important names in the Slavín at Vyšehrad, in the Lesser Town Cemetery in Košíře, and in the New Jewish Cemetery, just as in the Old Jewish Cemetery. Here people have classified them. Names are recalled with titles and with the significance of old families and merits. Then the centuries pass and all flows together with heaven and earth, under the sign of the cross or the star of David. The Jewish cemeteries are especially interesting everywhere, outside of Prague as well. It is a shame that they are disappearing. The cemetery in Libeň was beautiful. It recalled especially those who created a piece *of their town along the Vltava, founded here their shops and trades, and transformed themselves from minor laborers to rich factory-owners. Today only their names live, in the street names in this part of Prague.*

The oldest and most interesting of all, of course, is the Old Jewish Cemetery in Prague, where we find the gravestone of Rabbi Löw, the Jewish scholar and philosopher from the time of Rudolf. It is said that he who places a piece of paper with a wish in a crevice in his gravestone will certainly see it fulfilled. I don't know. There have been many requests and wishes here, hopeless laments and longings. How many plaintiffs have stood by these stones, strangely carved into various shapes, marked with a star instead of a cross, because the cross is supposed to signify suffering, but the star, hope.

But one objects. How many stars have there already been that the world relied on? Five- and six-pointed, of various colors and meanings. By them the world has seen oaths, threats, and pleas. But the stars, too, are silent when little Miriam or Ester runs to the grave of the great rabbi so that he will speak to the Lord on their behalf in heaven, when their parents have been hauled away, and their brothers too, and they are hiding with good relatives. But they themselves are caught and taken away!

What all occurs to a person wandering through the former Jewish streets of the age-old city of Prague! What admiration one hears for the artistry of, for example, the gravestone in the New Jewish Cemetery where lies Louis Russ, or the gravestone of the painter Max Horb by the famous Czech sculptor Jan Štursa! All the constructive elements, architecturally shaped into artistic works of the first magnitude, structures of the last refuge on this Prague turf, from the Gothic through the Renaissance to Cubism, are an overview of the talents of creators and names. The old and the new Jewish Cemeteries are an interesting gallery and nobody wants to miss them in a visit to Prague. Here have remained the names of the celebrated lives of those who together loved this city, worked for it, and used it for common happiness.

The golem? Somebody allegedly encountered him as well. Or rather his shadow. Another asserted that he saw his fiery shem shining one evening in the foggy Prague autumn, and heard his steps as they resounded along the muffled pavement of the former ghetto.

Prague is a magical city, enchanting. That's why Charles IV, Rudolf II, and other kings and rulers fell in love with it. All who had the opportunity have longed for it. Tycho de Brahe, the astronomer of Rudolf II, who found his final rest in Prague's Týn Church, fell in love with it for the same reason.

People who come here as guests are always welcome. Praguers wear their hearts on their sleeves for them. But woe to those who come with other intentions. So far no attacks on our city have gone unpunished.

The golem? He is another story! Why, he had no heart! He served the one who controlled his shem. Prague, that beauty of all ages, has over the centuries of its existence won many hearts filled with love and poetry, and with music. Do you hear it? It sounds in all the churches, chapels, and synagogues. In it is a profession of faith, but also strength and resolution for the coming days. In the hands of its people it is ever more beautiful. In it is the endless prayer of past and future ages. The endlessly constant and great faith of humanity in mankind and mankind's Creator. Perhaps after all the sun of love will rise one day over all beings living here.